Kids

SUMMER ACADEMY

ARGOPREP

7 DAYS A WEEK

12 WEEKS

- Mathematics
- English
- Science
- Reading
- Writing
- Experiments
- Mazes
- Puzzles
- Fitness

GRADE 6-7

ArgoPrep is one of the leading providers of supplemental educational products and services. We offer affordable and effective test prep solutions to educators, parents and students. Learning should be fun and easy! To access more resources visit us at www.argoprep.com.

Our goal is to make your life easier, so let us know how we can help you by e-mailing us at: info@argoprep.com.

Want much more free worksheets?

Visit us at argoprep.com/worksheets

- ArgoPrep is a recipient of the prestigious **Mom's Choice Award**.
- ArgoPrep also received the 2019 **Seal of Approval** from Homeschool.com for our award-winning workbooks.
- ArgoPrep was awarded the 2019 **National Parenting Products Award, Gold Medal Parent's Choice Award** and **the Tillywig Brain Child Award**.

TABLE OF CONTENTS

TABLE OF CONTENTS

TABLE OF CONTENTS

TABLE OF CONTENTS

HOW TO USE THE BOOK

Welcome to **Kids Summer Academy** by ArgoPrep.

This workbook is designed to prepare students over the summer to get ready for **Grade 7.**
The curriculum has been divided into **twelve weeks** so students can complete this entire workbook over the summer.

Our workbook has been carefully designed and **crafted by licensed teachers** to give students an incredible learning experience.
Students start off the week with English activities followed by Math practice. Throughout the week, students have several fitness activities to complete. Making sure students stay active is just as important as practicing mathematics.
We introduce yoga and other basic fitness activities that any student can complete. Each week includes a science experiment which sparks creativity and allows students to visually understand the concepts. On the last day of each week, students will work on a fun puzzle.

HOW TO WATCH VIDEO EXPLANATIONS
IT IS ABSOLUTELY FREE

Download our app:
ArgoPrep Video Explanations
to access videos on any mobile device or tablet.

or

Step 1 - Visit our website at: www.argoprep.com/k8
Step 2 - Click on the Video Explanations button located on the top right corner.
Step 3 - Choose the workbook you have and enjoy video explanations.

WHAT TO READ OVER THE SUMMER

One of the best ways to increase your reading comprehension level is to read a book for at least **20** minutes a day. We strongly encourage students to read several books throughout the summer. Below you will find a recommended summer reading list that we have compiled for students entering into Grade 7 or simply visit us at: www. argobrothers.com/**summerlist**

Author: J. R. R. Tolkien
Title: The Hobbit

Author: Cynthia Voigt
Title: Homecoming

Author: Wendelin Van Draanen
Title: Flipped

Author: Margaret Gurevich
Title: Chloe by Design: Making the Cut

Author: Edward Bloor
Title: Tangerine

Author: Markus Zusak
Title: The Book Thief

Author: George Orwell
Title: Animal Farm

Author: S. E. Hinton
Title: The Outsiders

Author: M. T. Anderson
Title: Symphony for the City of the Dead

Author: Kwame Alexander
Title: The Crossover

BOOKS BY ARGOPREP

Here are some other test prep workbooks by ArgoPrep you may be interested in. All of our workbooks come equipped with detailed video explanations to make your learning experience a breeze! Visit us at www.argoprep.com

COMMON CORE MATH SERIES

COMMON CORE ELA SERIES

COMMON CORE TEST SERIES

The goal of these workbooks is to provide mock state tests so students can increase confidence and test scores during actual test day.

INTRODUCING MATH!

Introducing Math! by ArgoPrep is an award-winning series created by certified teachers to provide students with high-quality practice problems. Our workbooks include topic overviews with instruction, practice questions, answer explanations along with digital access to video explanations. Practice in confidence - with ArgoPrep!

KIDS SUMMER ACADEMY SERIES

ArgoPrep's **Kids Summer Academy** series helps prevent summer learning loss and gets students ready for their new school year by reinforcing core foundations in math, english and science. Our workbooks also introduce new concepts so students can get a head start and be on top of their game for the new school year!

WATER FIRE

DANCE HERO

ADRASTOS THE SUPER WARRIOR

MYSTICAL NINJA

GREEN POISON

CAPTAIN BRAVERY

RAPID NINJA

FIRESTORM WARRIOR

CAPTAIN ARGO

THUNDER WARRIOR

Give your character a name

_____

Write down the special ability or powers your character has and how you will help your community with the powers.

_____

_____

Great! You are all set. To become an incredible hero, we need to strengthen our skills in **English, math** and **science**. Let's get started.

WeeK 1

OVERVIEW OF ENGLISH CONCEPTS

Varying Sentence Length

You've spent the last few years ramping up the length and complexity of your writing from single sentences to multi-paragraph essays. Now that you have that foundation, this is a great time to reflect back on some crucial fundamentals that can strengthen your own writing and improve your skills as a reader.

One of the ways writers of both fiction and nonfiction keep their writing interesting and engaging is by **varying the lengths of sentences.** That means using a combination of short, medium, and long sentences to get your ideas across. When you write using only <u>short</u> sentences, it makes your writing feel <u>basic</u>, like you wrote it when you were very young. <u>Long</u> sentences can make your writing seem more mature, but they can also create places where readers can get <u>lost</u> or <u>confused</u>. That's why a strong writing approach involves **varying sentence length!**

As a Writer...
Here are a few tips to help make sure you're thinking about sentence length and variety of different sentences to engage and inform your audience:
- **Introduce ideas** using <u>short</u> sentences (This helps make sure your main ideas are **clear** for the reader.)
- **Discuss and explore those ideas** using <u>medium or long sentences</u> (This helps show your thinking and provides the reader with more detail than you can give using short sentences.)
- **Summarize and wrap ideas up** using <u>short or medium</u> sentences (Again, it's important to **maximize clarity!**)
- **Always double-check** your writing for a **variety of sentence lengths** (Read your work once over when you feel like you're done and try to notice if you're using sentences of the same approximate length and structure over and over again -- a few revisions can make a huge difference for you and the reader!)

As a Reader...
When you're reading other people's writing as a mature consumer, it's important to think about **how** the author makes their point **in addition to** deciphering their meaning. Here are a few strategies to help guide your thinking as you look at other people's sentences:
- **Notice the approximate length** of each sentence (short, medium, long) as you read (See if you can detect any **pattern** in the author's sentence structure or length.)
- **Underline, circle, or make note of** sentences that feel weak or confusing (Ask yourself: "What made this sentence stand out as weak? Is it too short? Too long? Too much like the ideas before it?" Etc.)
- **Learn from the mistakes** in the texts you read (When you notice a sentence that doesn't work, try to remember what you didn't like about it so you can avoid using similar sentences in your own work.)

From "Walden"

By Henry David Thoreau

When first I took up my abode in the woods, that is, began to spend my nights as well as days there, which, by accident, was on Independence Day, or the Fourth of July, 1845, my house was not finished for winter, but was merely a defence against the rain, without plastering or chimney, the walls being of rough, weather-stained boards, with wide gaps between them, which made it cool at night. The upright white hewn studs and freshly planed door and window casings gave it a clean and airy look, especially in the morning, when its timbers were saturated with dew, so that I fancied that by noon some sweet gum would exude from them. To my imagination it retained throughout the day more or less of this auroral character, reminding me of a certain house on a mountain which I had visited the year before. This was an airy and unplastered cabin, fit to entertain a travelling god, and where a goddess might trail her garments. The winds which passed over my dwelling were such as sweep over the ridges of mountains, bearing the broken strains, or celestial parts only, of terrestrial music. The morning wind forever blows, the poem of creation is uninterrupted; but few are the ears that hear it. Olympus is but the outside of the earth every where.

The only house I had been the owner of before, if I except a boat, was a tent, which I used occasionally when making excursions in the summer, and this is still rolled up in my garret; but the boat, after passing from hand to hand, has gone down the stream of time. With this more substantial shelter about me, I had made some progress toward settling in the world. This frame, so slightly clad, was a sort of crystallization around me, and reacted on the builder. It was suggestive somewhat as a picture in outlines. I did not need to go outdoors to take the air, for the atmosphere within had lost none of its freshness. It was not so much within doors as behind a door where I sat, even in the rainiest weather. The Harivansa says, "An abode without birds is like a meat without seasoning." Such was not my abode, for I found myself suddenly neighbor to the birds; not by having imprisoned one, but having caged myself near them. I was not only nearer to some of those which commonly frequent the garden and the orchard, but to those wilder and more thrilling songsters of the forest which never, or rarely, serenade a villager, — the wood-thrush, the veery, the scarlet tanager, the field-sparrow, the whippoorwill, and many others.

I. Describe the narrator's **living situation** in the text:

_____

_____

_____

2. Based on the passage, how would you describe the narrator's **personality?** How does he seem to view the world?

_____

_____

_____

_____

3. **True** or **False**: The narrator's cabin is the first home he's ever owned.

   A. **False:** He had a home in the village.
   B. **True:** He only owned a boat and a tent before.
   C. **False:** He is rich and owns many homes.
   D. **True:** The narrator recently got out of prison.

4. How would you describe the author's **sentence length** in this passage?

   A. The author writes short sentences to maximize clarity.
   B. The author alternates long and short sentences to provide variety.
   C. The author writes long sentences that use a lot of commas to help the reader visualize action.
   D. The author writes long sentences that use a lot of commas to provide a lot of detail.

5. Why does the narrator say he "caged [himself] near" the **birds?** How is his living situation different from the way most people interact with birds?

_____

_____

_____

_____

Noticing Sentence Length

Directions: Read each paragraph below closely, observing the length of the sentences as you read. Answer the questions below each paragraph to suggest ways that the sentence variety could be improved or strengthened.

My favorite activity is playing rugby, which I discovered during a family trip to England. Rugby is sort of like a combination of American football and soccer, but it's a lot more complex than that. The most well-known aspect of rugby is its physicality, which takes the form of full-contact tackling and desperate dogpiles of players competing for the ball.

1. How would you describe the **variety** of sentences in this paragraph?

   A. This paragraph contains sentences of different lengths and structures.
   B. All the sentences in this paragraph have approximately the same length and structure.
   C. The author eases the reader into ideas with a shorter sentence, then develops the ideas more fully with longer sentences.
   D. The author introduces complex ideas using longer sentences, then explains things one step at a time using shorter sentences.

2. How could you change the first sentence of this passage to provide greater variety of sentences in the passage? How could you break those ideas up into some shorter sentences that could <u>ease the reader into</u> the paragraph?

   _____

   _____

   _____

   _____

Driving in snowy or icy conditions can be very difficult and nerve-wracking. If your car does not have four-wheel drive or the right tires, your car may have difficulty grabbing the road properly. This can create any number of dangerous scenarios. For example, with the slightest turn of the wheel or tap of the brakes, you could begin to skid or spin out. Luckily, disaster is completely avoidable. If you know snow is in the forecast, just stay home!

3. How would you describe the **variety** of sentences in this paragraph?

   A. This paragraph contains sentences of different lengths and structures.
   B. All the sentences in this paragraph have approximately the same length and structure.
   C. The author eases the reader into ideas with a shorter sentence, then develops the ideas more fully with longer sentences.
   D. The author introduces complex ideas using longer sentences, then explains things one step at a time using shorter sentences.

4. **First**, underline the sentence in the paragraph that you feel is the weakest or in the most need of being shortened or lengthened. Then, rewrite the sentence as you see fit on the lines below:

_____

_____

_____

_____

fitness

Please be aware of your environment and be safe at all times. If you cannot do an exercise, just try your best.

Repeat these **exercises 4 ROUNDS**

2 - Lunges: 8 times to each leg.
Note: Use your body weight or books as weight to do leg lunges.

1 - Abs: 20 times

4 - Run: 50m
Note: Run 25 meters to one side and 25 meters back to the starting position.

3 - Plank: 20 sec.

From "Walden"

By Henry David Thoreau

(Continued from Day 1's Passage)

I went to the woods because I wished to live deliberately, to front only the essential facts of life, and see if I could not learn what it had to teach, and not, when I came to die, discover that I had not lived. I did not wish to live what was not life, living is so dear; nor did I wish to practice resignation, unless it was quite necessary. I wanted to live deep and suck out all the marrow of life, to live so sturdily and Spartan-like as to put to rout all that was not life, to cut a broad swath and shave close, to drive life into a corner, and reduce it to its lowest terms, and, if it proved to be mean, why then to get the whole and genuine meanness of it, and publish its meanness to the world; or if it were sublime, to know it by experience, and be able to give a true account of it in my next excursion. For most men, it appears to me, are in a strange uncertainty about it, whether it is of the devil or of God, and have somewhat hastily concluded that it is the chief end of man here to "glorify God and enjoy him forever."

Still we live meanly, like ants; though the fable tells us that we were long ago changed into men; like pygmies we fight with cranes; it is error upon error, and clout upon clout, and our best virtue has for its occasion a superfluous and evitable wretchedness. Our life is frittered away by detail. An honest man has hardly need to count more than his ten fingers, or in extreme cases he may add his ten toes, and lump the rest. Simplicity, simplicity, simplicity! I say, let your affairs be as two or three, and not a hundred or a thousand; instead of a million count half a dozen, and keep your accounts on your thumb nail. In the midst of this chopping sea of civilized life, such are the clouds and storms and quicksands and thousand-and-one items to be allowed for, that a man has to live, if he would not founder and go to the bottom and not make his port at all, by dead reckoning, and he must be a great calculator indeed who succeeds. Simplify, simplify.

1. What does the author mean when he says he wants to live **"Spartan-like"** and reduce life **"to its lowest terms"**? (It might be helpful to reflect on ideas from Day 1's passage as well!)

_____

_____

2. According to the author, **why** is he conducting this experiment that involves living in the woods?

_____

_____

3. Why does the author bring up **God** and the **devil**?

   A. He believes religion is crucial to the improvement of our lives and society.
   B. He believes that not enough people question the true purpose and importance of life.
   C. He believes the struggle between God and the devil is depicted in nature.
   D. He believes the struggle between God and the devil is depicted by the daily life that most people live in cities.

4. How does the author believe people can improve their lives (and the world)?

   A. By thinking and living on a more grandiose scale
   B. By thinking about and living in nature more
   C. By thinking and living on a much simpler scale
   D. By thinking about and living based on the teachings of religion

5. Do you agree with the author's emphasis on **simplicity** in life? <u>Why</u> or why not? Be sure to explain your thinking and give examples to back yourself up.

_____

_____

_____

_____

_____

Writing a Paragraph While Varying Sentence Length

Directions: Read the writing prompt below and craft a response of **at least five sentences** on the lines below. Demonstrate your mastery of sentence length by doing the following:
- Introduce main ideas with short, clear sentences
- Use longer sentences (and commas) to provide a variety of well-explained details
- Provide a variety of sentences (try to write <u>at least two short, impactful sentences</u> and <u>at least two longer, more detailed sentences)</u>

PROMPT: Do you think you would be able to live in the woods on your own like Henry David Thoreau did before he published "Walden?" Why or why not?

_____

_____

_____

_____

_____

_____

_____

_____

_____

_____

_____

_____

_____

_____

_____

_____

_____

_____

_____

_____

_____

_____

_____

fitness

Please be aware of your environment and be safe at all times. If you cannot do an exercise, just try your best.

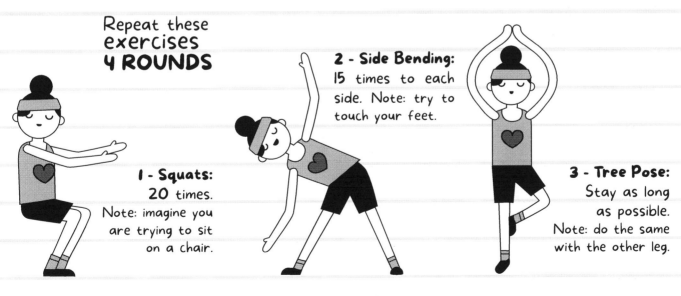

Repeat these **exercises 4 ROUNDS**

1 - Squats: 20 times. Note: imagine you are trying to sit on a chair.

2 - Side Bending: 15 times to each side. Note: try to touch your feet.

3 - Tree Pose: Stay as long as possible. Note: do the same with the other leg.

Ratios and Percents

1. What is the ratio of circles to triangles?

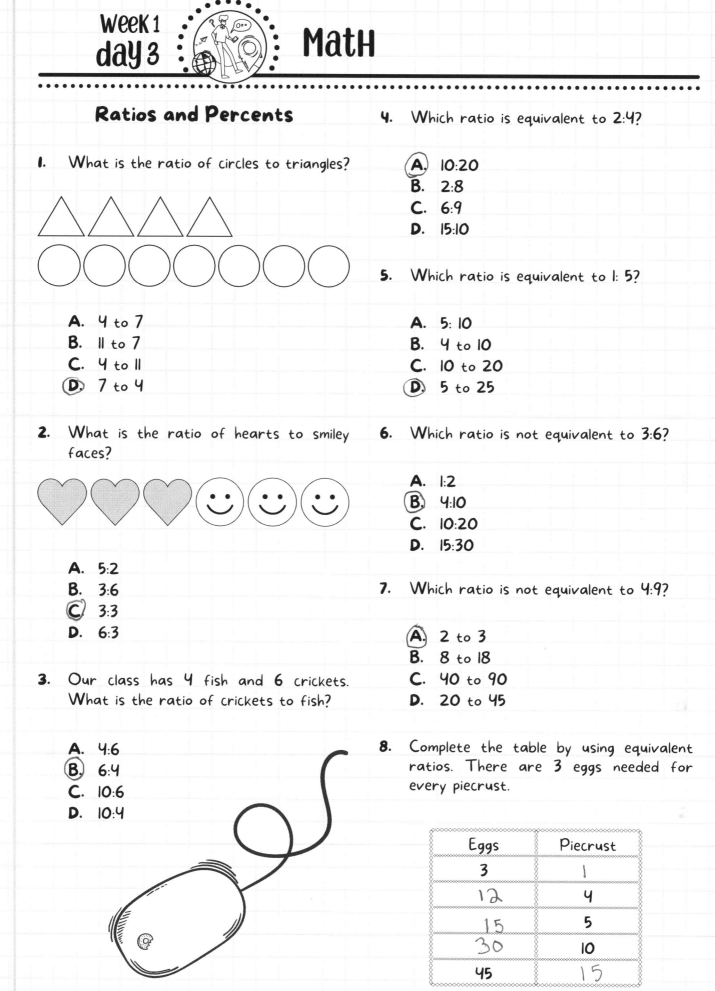

A. 4 to 7
B. 11 to 7
C. 4 to 11
D. 7 to 4

2. What is the ratio of hearts to smiley faces?

A. 5:2
B. 3:6
C. 3:3
D. 6:3

3. Our class has 4 fish and 6 crickets. What is the ratio of crickets to fish?

A. 4:6
B. 6:4
C. 10:6
D. 10:4

4. Which ratio is equivalent to 2:4?

A. 10:20
B. 2:8
C. 6:9
D. 15:10

5. Which ratio is equivalent to 1: 5?

A. 5: 10
B. 4 to 10
C. 10 to 20
D. 5 to 25

6. Which ratio is not equivalent to 3:6?

A. 1:2
B. 4:10
C. 10:20
D. 15:30

7. Which ratio is not equivalent to 4:9?

A. 2 to 3
B. 8 to 18
C. 40 to 90
D. 20 to 45

8. Complete the table by using equivalent ratios. There are 3 eggs needed for every piecrust.

Eggs	Piecrust
3	1
12	4
15	5
30	10
45	15

9. A train carries 768 passengers every day. If it makes 4 trips an hour and runs for six hours, how many passengers does the train carry each trip?

A. 28
B. 30
C. 32
D. 34

10. Justin replaces all four tires in his car for $872. How much does each tire cost?

A. $218
B. $220
C. $224
D. $228

11. Herbert fills his gas tank for $53.46. If he has an 18-gallon tank, how much does each gallon of gas cost?

A. $2.96
B. $2.97
C. $2.98
D. $2.99

 fitness

Please be aware of your environment and be safe at all times. If you cannot do an exercise, just try your best.

Repeat these **exercises 4 ROUNDS**

1 - Bend forward: 15 times.
Note: try to touch your feet. Make sure to keep your back straight and if needed you can bend your knees.

2 - Lunges: 12 times to each leg.
Note: Use your body weight or books as weight to do leg lunges.

3 - Plank: 20 sec.

4 - Abs: 20 times

Ratios and Percents

1. Alicia walked 3 miles in 90 minutes. How many miles did she walk in an hour?

- **A.** 2 miles
- **B.** 1 mile
- **C.** 1.5 miles
- **D.** 0.5 miles

2. Thomas bought 5 bags of popcorn for $8.75. How much did one bag of popcorn cost?

- **A.** $1.75
- **B.** $1.50
- **C.** $1.25
- **D.** $8.75

3. Which bag of coffee beans is the best deal?

- **A.** $25.20 for three pounds
- **B.** $17.33 for 2 pounds
- **C.** $6.22 for half a pound
- **D.** $8.26 for a pound

4. Evelyn read 216 pages in 3 hours. How many pages did she read every half hour?

- **A.** 72 pages
- **B.** 36 pages
- **C.** 18 pages
- **D.** 100 pages

5. A truck travels 512 miles in 8 hours. How many miles does the truck travel every hour?

- **A.** 60
- **B.** 62
- **C.** 64
- **D.** 66

6. Which hotel room is the most expensive per night?

- **A.** 3 nights for $267
- **B.** 2 nights for $182
- **C.** 4 nights for $385
- **D.** 1 night for $95

7. Which hotel room is the cheapest per night?

- **A.** 3 nights for $234
- **B.** 3 nights for $222
- **C.** 2 nights for $164
- **D.** 1 night for $101

8. Who scored the most points per game?

- **A.** Benjamin scored 12 points in 1 game
- **B.** Daniel scored 40 points in 4 games.
- **C.** Jose scored 36 points in 2 games.
- **D.** Joshua scored 45 points in 3 games.

9. Who had the slowest race time?

- **A.** Laura ran 2 miles in 17 minutes.
- **B.** Ashley ran one mile in 6.5 minutes.
- **C.** Mary ran 3 miles in 21.75 minutes.
- **D.** Jen ran one mile in 8 minutes.

10. Who is the fastest typer?

- **A.** Alex types 105 words in 3 minutes.
- **B.** David types 90 words in 2 minutes.
- **C.** Kara types 160 words in 4 minutes.
- **D.** Emily types 252 words in 6 minutes.

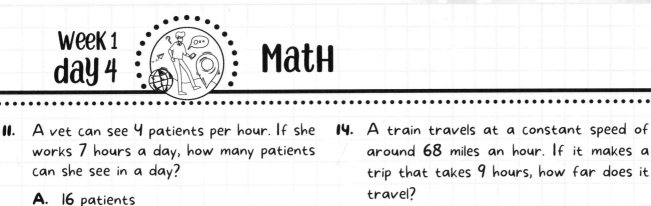
11. A vet can see 4 patients per hour. If she works 7 hours a day, how many patients can she see in a day?

A. 16 patients
B. 20 patients
C. 24 patients
D. 28 patients

12. At the grocery store, 7 oranges cost $1.75. How much would 16 oranges cost?

A. $1   C. $3
B. $2   D. $4

13. Our bus driver delivers 36 students home in 45 minutes. If he stops the bus every 5 minutes to let an equal number of students off, how many students get off at each stop?

A. 4 students   C. 6 students
B. 5 students   D. 7 students

14. A train travels at a constant speed of around 68 miles an hour. If it makes a trip that takes 9 hours, how far does it travel?

A. 620 miles   C. 610 miles
B. 612 miles   D. 602 miles

15. A train travels at a constant speed and goes 434 miles in 7 hours. If it maintains that pace, how far does it travel in 10 hours?

A. 606 miles
B. 614 miles
C. 620 miles
D. 624 miles

fitness

Please be aware of your environment and be safe at all times. If you cannot do an exercise, just try your best.

Repeat these
exercises
4 ROUNDS

1 - High Plank: 25 sec.

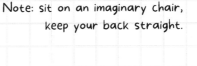

2 - Chair: 20 sec.
Note: sit on an imaginary chair, keep your back straight.

3 - Waist Hooping: 20 times. Note: if you do not have a hoop, pretend you have an imaginary hoop and rotate your hips 10 times.

4 - Abs: 25 times

Ratios and Percents

1. What percent is represented by the shaded area?

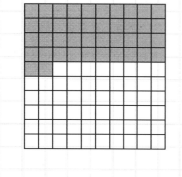

A. 42%   C. 46%
B. 58%   D. 52%

2. What percent is represented by the shaded area?

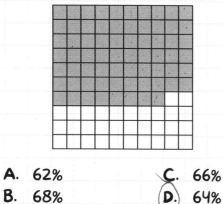

A. 62%   C. 66%
B. 68%   D. 64%

3. What percent is represented by the shaded area?

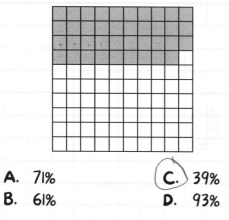

A. 71%   C. 39%
B. 61%   D. 93%

4. What percent is represented by the shaded area?

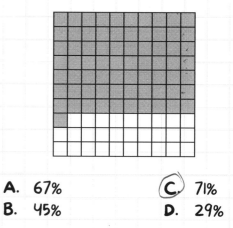

A. 67%   C. 71%
B. 45%   D. 29%

5. What percent is represented by the shaded area?

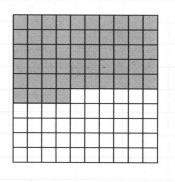

A. 45%   C. 68%
B. 54%   D. 92%

6. What is 24% of 200?

A. 48   C. 56
B. 52   D. 62

7. What is 30% of 120?

A. 34   C. 38
B. 36   D. 40

8. What is 62% of 250?

   A. 155   C. 165
   B. 160   D. 170

9. What is 15% of 180?

   A. 23   C. 27
   B. 25   D. 29

10. What is 80% of 350?

    A. 220   C. 260
    B. 240   D. 280

11. In our class, 12 out of 26 students have a dog. What percent of students have a dog?

    A. 46%   C. 50%
    B. 48%   D. 52%

12. In our town, there are 6 parks. Four out of six of them have a sandbox. What percent of parks do NOT have a sandbox?

    A. 11%   B. 33%

        C. 66%   D. 99%

13. You are trying to download a video game and it is 20% downloaded. You have downloaded 16,000 kilobytes so far. How big is the total file in kilobytes?

    A. 60,000   C. 100,000
    B. 80,000   D. 110,000

14. Last month, my father exercised 18 out of 30 days. What percent of the month did he exercise?

    A. 60%   C. 70%
    B. 80%   D. 90%

15. Our library hosts family movie nights. 60% of those who attend are children. If 108 children attended last night, how many total people were there?

    A. 180
    B. 170
    C. 160
    D. 150

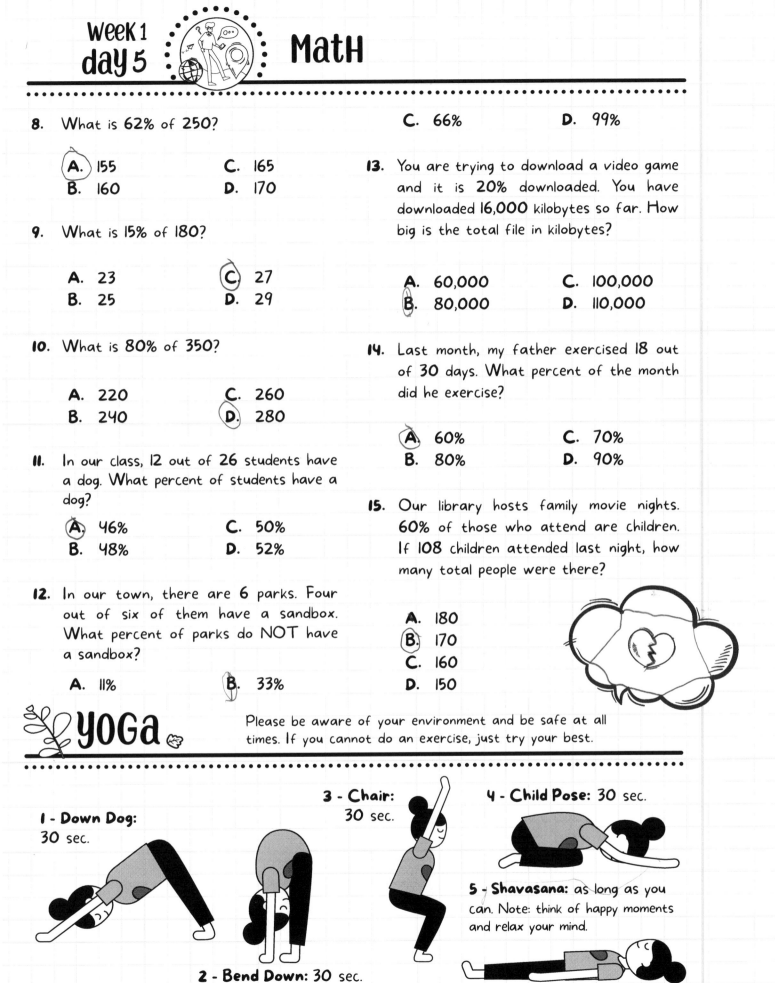

yoga

Please be aware of your environment and be safe at all times. If you cannot do an exercise, just try your best.

1 - Down Dog: 30 sec.

2 - Bend Down: 30 sec.

3 - Chair: 30 sec.

4 - Child Pose: 30 sec.

5 - Shavasana: as long as you can. Note: think of happy moments and relax your mind.

Population, Community, & Ecosystem

Over the next few weeks, we'll be doing a series of activities related to **natural science**, which is the study of how different animals, plants, and other things interact in the physical world. In order to do so, we need to start by defining three important words: **population**, **community**, and **ecosystem**. A **population** is a group of organisms (animals or plants) who are the <u>same species</u> and live in the <u>same area</u>. A **community** is the collection of all the different **populations** that live in a given area. That entire community <u>plus all the non-living things in the environment</u> is collectively known as an **ecosystem**.

A great way to explain this concept is using **school!** Each grade level or class can be thought of as a **population**. All those students added together along with the teachers and other employees of the school make up the school **community**. When you think about the area that community lives and works (the school with all its classrooms, playing fields, etc.) that is the **ecosystem!**

We'll start our science activities this year by thinking about our **home ecosystem!**

Materials:

- Notepaper
- A few pieces of plain white paper
- Art supplies (crayons, markers, colored pencils, etc.)

Procedure:

1. Take a piece of notepaper and **brainstorm** all the different people and animals who live with you. This should include you, any siblings or other family members you live with, your parents/guardians, and any pets or animals you own (even goldfish!).

2. Once you've identified all the individuals in your house, take some time to **draw a picture** of each person or animal on a piece of plain paper using your art supplies.

3. After you have created pictures for all the people and animals you live with, take some time to group those pictures into **populations**. Start by creating a population of **humans** who live in your house or apartment. Depending on how many pets or animals you have, this could include all the individuals you brainstormed or just some of them.

4. Once you have grouped all your **humans**, think about how you would group the populations of any remaining animals living with you. If you have two dogs or two fish, you can group those together into a population. Remember, you shouldn't group a cat and a dog together as pets because a **population** is made up of one species.

5. Take a minute to think about the area **outside** your home. Are there any other populations of animals that are noticeable? Think about birds, squirrels, raccoons, or other forms of wildlife that you know come near your living space. If you want, you can create pictures for these as well.

6. Now that your populations are complete, it's time to think about the **community**. Group your pictures together to create a **community** of organisms that live inside your house. This should include all people and pets. If you created cards for wild animals that live outside, you can also group those into a **community** of outdoor animals.

7. Finally, it's time to think about the **ecosystem** in which you and these other organisms all live. Using a piece of paper, draw a picture of the location in which you and the other members of your **community** live. Remember: the ecosystem involves both living and non-living things, so things like furniture and even rocks are definitely part of the ecosystem! If you created pictures for outdoors animals as well, you can draw a picture that shows the outdoor ecosystem they live in around your house.

8. Answer the questions below and clean up your materials.

Follow-Up Questions:

1. What kinds of organisms (plants or animals) did you identify in your community or ecosystem **other than humans?**

_____

_____

_____

2. Based on the activity you did today, explain how multiple **populations** can live together in one **community**:

_____

_____

yoga

Please be aware of your environment and be safe at all times. If you cannot do an exercise, just try your best.

3 - Stretching: Stay as long as possible. Note: do on one leg then on another.

2 - Down Dog: 30 sec.

4 - Lower Plank: 20 sec. Note: Keep your back straight and body tight.

1 - Tree Pose: Stay as long as possible. Note: do on one leg then on another.

6 - Shavasana: 5 min. Note: this pose is very important and provides you with long term benefits. Try not to skip this. Close your eyes and imagine who you want to be and what your goals are! Always think happy thoughts.

5 - Book Pose: 20 sec. Note: Keep your core tight. Legs should be across from your eyes.

Task: Help Joe find his way to Sarah through the maze. Color in the path and don't get lost!.

week 2

Writing Purposeful Sentences

Last week, we discussed the idea of **sentence length,** and you saw some examples of how repetitive sentence length can make a text harder to follow or stay interested in. This week, we'll look at another fundamental idea about the sentences in your paragraph.

Each sentence you write should be **purposeful.** That means it's doing an **important job** to communicate information to your reader. Sentences that aren't purposeful should be corrected to serve a function in their paragraph or removed outright. Let's take a look at some of the different "purposes" sentences serve.

The Purposes of Sentences:

Every sentence you read or write should perform one of the following jobs:

- **Introducing ideas** (As we said last week, these sentences should emphasize <u>clarity</u>.)
- **Explaining or describing** ideas, people, or events that are relevant to the text (As we said last week, these sentences should be a little longer and emphasize <u>detail</u>.)
- **Providing examples or evidence** that lend support for what the author is saying
- **Connecting ideas** and showing how various aspects of the topic or story are related to each other
- **Summarizing main ideas** to remind the reader what they've learned and help them keep track of all the different information contained in the text

Thinking About Sentences as a Reader:

However, understanding the purpose of different sentences isn't just about improving your writing. It's also about making you a better, more effective reader. When you read a sentence, ask yourself:

- What does the sentence **say?** (What do the words literally mean?)
- What is the **purpose** of this sentence? (Use the above list to help guide your thinking.)
- Is the sentence **fulfilling** that purpose effectively? (Does it introduce a topic clearly? Does it provide effective, easy-to-understand support? If not, what should the sentence be doing better? How would you, as a writer, change it?)
- Do all the sentences work together to form a **cohesive paragraph?** (Ask yourself, "Is anything missing?")

Once you begin to read texts through this sentence-by-sentence lens, you'll find it easier to dig deep into texts and determine whether you really agree with or enjoy them. While it sounds like a lot of work at first, thinking about the purpose of each sentence is truly the best way to review a text.

From "Walden"

By Henry David Thoreau

(Continued from Week 1's Passages)
(**NOTE:** a "sleeper" as it is used in this passage is what we would call a "railroad tie" today. It's one of the wooden crossbeams underneath the metal rails.)

The nation itself, with all its so called internal improvements, which, by the way are all external and superficial, is just such an unwieldy and overgrown establishment, cluttered with furniture and tripped up by its own traps, ruined by luxury and heedless expense, by want of calculation and a worthy aim, as the million households in the land; and the only cure for it as for them is in a rigid economy, a stern and more than Spartan simplicity of life and elevation of purpose. It lives too fast.

Men think that it is essential that the Nation have commerce, and export ice, and talk through a telegraph, and ride thirty miles an hour, without a doubt, whether they do or not; but whether we should live like baboons or like men, is a little uncertain. If we do not get out sleepers, and forge rails, and devote days and nights to the work, but go to tinkering upon our lives to improve them, who will build railroads? And if railroads are not built, how shall we get to heaven in season? But if we stay at home and mind our business, who will want railroads? We do not ride on the railroad; it rides upon us. Did you ever think what those sleepers are that underlie the railroad? Each one is a man, an Irish-man, or a Yankee man. The rails are laid on them, and they are covered with sand, and the cars run smoothly over them. They are sound sleepers, I assure you. And every few years a new lot is laid down and run over; so that, if some have the pleasure of riding on a rail, others have the misfortune to be ridden upon. And when they run over a man that is walking in his sleep, a supernumerary sleeper in the wrong position, and wake him up, they suddenly stop the cars, and make a hue and cry about it, as if this were an exception. I am glad to know that it takes a gang of men for every five miles to keep the sleepers down and level in their beds as it is, for this is a sign that they may sometime get up again.

Why should we live with such hurry and waste of life? We are determined to be starved before we are hungry. Men say that a stitch in time saves nine, and so they take a thousand stitches to-day to save nine to-morrow.

1. Based on Paragraph 1, what is the author's opinion of **government**?

_____

_____

2. What does the author mean when he writes, "We do not ride on the railroad; **it rides upon us**"?

_____

_____

3. What is the purpose of the sentence "It lives too fast," at the end of Paragraph 1?

   A. To summarize the ideas above it
   B. To provide an example that supports the main point
   C. To break the tension by making a joke
   D. To introduce a new idea

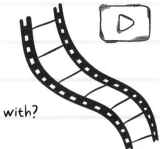

4. Which of these statements would the author **most likely** agree with?

   A. The train is the most important invention of all time.
   B. When you build something, you should hope that it lasts forever.
   C. People should question the true purpose and value of their work more often.
   D. Trains serve no purpose.

5. Do you <u>agree</u> or <u>disagree</u> with the author that people should stop focusing so much on the overall success of their **country**? Why or why not?

_____

_____

_____

_____

_____

Identifying the Purpose of Sentences

Directions: Read each short paragraph below and think about the **job** each sentence is performing as you read. Then answer the questions below each paragraph

(1) I think Arianna will probably win our school geography bee this year. (2) Last year, when she was in seventh grade, she finished second, and she's only become a better social studies student since then. (3) During the in-class qualifying round, she answered 15 questions, while most of the kids were out by the fourth round. (4) My only concern is that, even though she is very knowledgeable, she gets nervous under pressure sometimes. (5) If she wins, I am planning on going to the state bee to support her as well because we are best friends.

1. Which of these tasks is **not** accomplished by Sentence 2?

    A. Helping the reader understand how old Arianna is
    B. Helping the reader understand Arianna's prior experiences
    C. Helping the reader understand Arianna's work ethic
    D. Helping the reader understand the narrator's relationship to Arianna

2. Choose one of the sentences above (**except for Sentence 5**) and **rewrite it** to make the relationship between Arianna and the narrator **more clear,** so that the fact that they are friends is brought up before the final sentence.

_____

_____

_____

_____

(1) There are many different strategies that you can use to help you remember what you've read. (2) One of the most straightforward strategies is to take notes while you're writing. (3) This might not sound like fun for everyone at first, but writing things down in your own handwriting actually taps into the way your memory is wired to double-down on the chances that you'll remember something. (4) Discussing what you're reading with somebody else is helpful too. (5) Even if you're not in class, reading and discussing a text with friends is a good way to improve your comprehension and cash in on things that other people noticed that you might not have caught. (6) Another great strategy is to skim the text once through first, then go back to the beginning and read the whole thing closely.

3. Based on the structure of the paragraph, what should be added **after** Sentence 6?

    A. A general wrap-up statement that summarizes everything above
    B. An explanation of how or why the strategy described in Sentence **6** can be useful
    C. Another strategy that you can use to help you remember what you've read
    D. A few examples of the different kinds of texts you can apply these strategy to

4. <u>**Write a sentence**</u> that could go between Sentence 1 and Sentence 2 to help the reader understand why the strategies in Sentences **2-6** are so valuable or important:

_____

_____

_____

fitness

Please be aware of your environment and be safe at all times. If you cannot do an exercise, just try your best.

Repeat these **exercises 4 ROUNDS**

1 - Abs: 20 times

2 - Lunges: 8 times to each leg. Note: Use your body weight or books as weight to do leg lunges.

3 - Plank: 20 sec.

4 - Run: 50m Note: Run 25 meters to one side and 25 meters back to the starting position.

From "Walden"

By Henry David Thoreau

(Continued from Day 1's Passage. This part of "Walden" focuses on some of the things Thoreau did while he lived in the woods.)

With a little more deliberation in the choice of their pursuits, all men would perhaps become essentially students and observers, for certainly their nature and destiny are interesting to all alike. In accumulating property for ourselves or our posterity, in founding a family or a state, or acquiring fame even, we are mortal; but in dealing with truth we are immortal, and need fear no change nor accident. The oldest Egyptian or Hindu philosopher raised a corner of the veil from the statue of the divinity; and still the trembling robe remains raised, and I gaze upon as fresh a glory as he did, since it was I in him that was then so bold, and it is he in me that now reviews the vision. No dust has settled on that robe; no time has elapsed since that divinity was revealed. That time which we really improve, or which is improvable, is neither past, present, nor future.

My residence was more favorable, not only to thought, but to serious reading, than a university; and though I was beyond the range of the ordinary circulating library, I had more than ever come within the influence of those books which circulate round the world, whose sentences were first written on bark, and are now merely copied from time to time on to linen paper. Says the poet Mîr Camar Uddîn Mast, "Being seated to run through the region of the spiritual world; I have had this advantage in books. To be intoxicated by a single glass of wine; I have experienced this pleasure when I have drunk the liquor of the esoteric doctrines." I kept Homer's Iliad on my table through the summer, though I looked at his page only now and then. Incessant labor with my hands, at first, for I had my house to finish and my beans to hoe at the same time, made more study impossible. Yet I sustained myself by the prospect of such reading in future. I read one or two shallow books of travel in the intervals of my work, till that employment made me ashamed of myself, and I asked where it was then that I lived.

1. How does the **first sentence** of this passage connect to ideas from **Day 1's Passage** from the same book?

_____

_____

2. What does the author mean when he says, "In accumulating property for ourselves or our posterity, in founding a family or a state, or acquiring fame even, we are **mortal**; but in dealing with truth we are **immortal**"?

_____

_____

3. What is the purpose of the first sentence of Paragraph 2?

A. To signal a transition from general discussion of ideas toward examples from the author's own experience
B. To signal a transition from examples from the author's own experience toward general discussion of ideas
C. To remind the reader of the overall topic or point of the passage
D. To give an example of a place where reading is powerful

4. Which of these describes the connection between <u>reading</u> and <u>working on the cabin</u> in the narrator's experience?

A. The narrator reads a lot of thought-provoking books while he is working on the cabin.
B. When the narrator is reading something interesting, he does great work on the cabin. When he is reading something boring, he does low-quality work on the cabin.
C. The narrator struggles to read deep, thought-provoking books while he is working and mostly focuses on shallow travel books.
D. When the narrator is reading something interesting, he does low-quality work on the cabin. When he is reading something boring, he does great work on the cabin.

5. The author quotes a poet who said that enjoying a good book is like being "intoxicated by a single glass of wine." How do <u>you</u> feel about reading? Does it make you happy? Do you find it boring? Are there certain things you love to read about or certain genres you enjoy?

_____

_____

_____

_____

Writing a Paragraph with Only Purposeful Sentences

Directions: Read the writing prompt below and craft a response of **at least five sentences** on the lines below. Be sure all your sentences have **a clear purpose**.

PROMPT: Which do you think is more important: to be a great individual, or to be a citizen of a great country? Explain your thinking on the lines below.

_____

_____

_____

_____

_____

_____

_____

_____

_____

_____

_____

_____

_____

_____

_____

_____

_____

_____

_____

_____

_____

_____

_____

_____

Once you're done, be sure to **PROOFREAD** your paragraph and make sure that every sentence is either...

- Introducing main ideas
- Providing examples or evidence
- Explaining or contextualizing an example
- Connecting ideas
- Summarizing/Wrapping up ideas

fitness

Please be aware of your environment and be safe at all times. If you cannot do an exercise, just try your best.

Repeat these **exercises 4 ROUNDS**

2 - Side Bending: 15 times to each side. Note: try to touch your feet.

1 - Squats: 20 times. Note: imagine you are trying to sit on a chair.

3 - Tree Pose: Stay as long as possible. Note: do the same with the other leg.

Ratios and Percents

1. What amount <u>incorrectly</u> represents the shaded area?

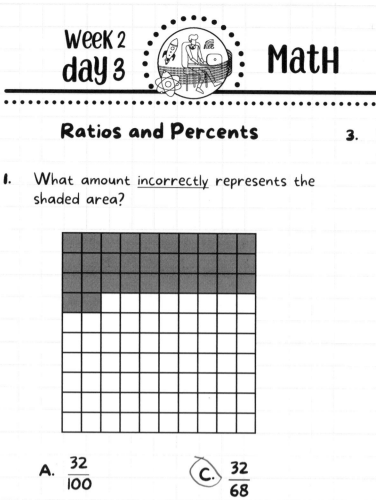

A. $\frac{32}{100}$ (C.) $\frac{32}{68}$

B. 0.32   D. 32%

2. What amount <u>incorrectly</u> represents the shaded area?

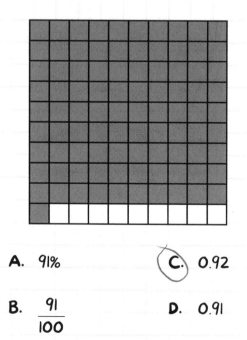

A. 91%   (C.) 0.92

B. $\frac{91}{100}$ D. 0.91

3. What amount <u>incorrectly</u> represents the shaded area?

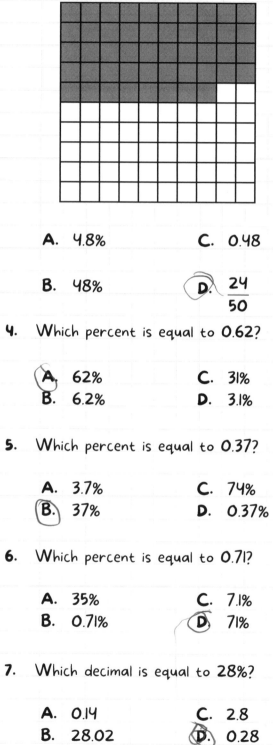

A. 4.8%   C. 0.48

B. 48%   (D.) $\frac{24}{50}$

4. Which percent is equal to 0.62?

(A.) 62%   C. 31%

B. 6.2%   D. 3.1%

5. Which percent is equal to 0.37?

A. 3.7%   C. 74%

(B.) 37%   D. 0.37%

6. Which percent is equal to 0.71?

A. 35%   C. 7.1%

B. 0.71%   (D.) 71%

7. Which decimal is equal to 28%?

A. 0.14   C. 2.8

B. 28.02   (D.) 0.28

8. Which decimal is equal to 94%?

   A. 0.96   C. 0.98
   (B.) 0.94   D. 0.96

9. Which decimal is equal to 85%?

   (A.) 0.85   C. 0.45
   B. 0.8   D. 0.32

10. Which percent is equal to $\frac{38}{100}$?

    (A.) 38%   C. 42%
    B. 40%   D. 62%

11. Which percent is equal to $\frac{33}{50}$?

    (A.) 33%   C. 99%
    B. 66%   D. 50%

12. Which percent is equal to $\frac{7}{25}$?

    A. 36%   (C.) 28%
    B. 32%   D. 24%

13. Which fraction is equal to 21%?

    (A.) $\frac{21}{100}$ C. $\frac{82}{100}$

    B. $\frac{44}{100}$ D. $\frac{48}{50}$

14. Which fraction is equal to 14%?

    A. $\frac{4}{20}$ C. $\frac{13}{100}$

    (B.) $\frac{14}{20}$ D. $\frac{7}{50}$

15. Which fraction is equal to 79%?

    A. $\frac{36}{100}$ (C.) $\frac{79}{100}$

    B. $\frac{42}{100}$ D. $\frac{97}{100}$

fitness

Please be aware of your environment and be safe at all times. If you cannot do an exercise, just try your best.

Repeat these exercises **4 ROUNDS**

2 - Lunges: 12 times to each leg.
Note: Use your body weight or books as weight to do leg lunges.

3 - Plank: 20 sec.

1 - Bend forward: 15 times.
Note: try to touch your feet. Make sure to keep your back straight and if needed you can bend your knees.

4 - Abs: 20 times

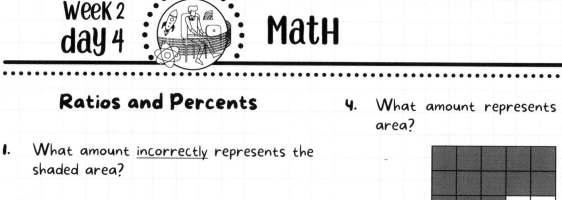

Ratios and Percents

1. What amount <u>incorrectly</u> represents the shaded area?

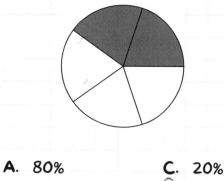

    Ⓐ. 4%   C. 0.4

    B. 40%   D. $\frac{4}{10}$

2. What amount represents the shaded area?

    A. 80%   C. 20%

    B. 60%   Ⓓ. 40%

3. What amount represents the shaded area?

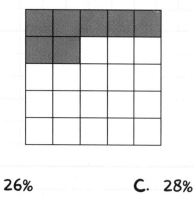

    Ⓐ. 26%   C. 28%

    B. 7%   D. 22%

4. What amount represents the shaded area?

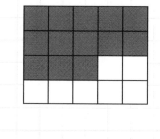

    A. 60%   C. 70%

    Ⓑ. 65%   D. 75%

5. What amount represents the shaded area?

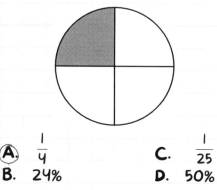

    Ⓐ. $\frac{1}{4}$ C. $\frac{1}{25}$

    B. 24%   D. 50%

6. How many sections of a shape would you shade to represent **20%** if the shape was divided into **5** equal parts?

    A. 3   Ⓒ. 1

    B. 4   D. 2

7. How many sections of a shape would you shade to represent **30%** if the shape was divided into **30** equal parts?

    A. 6   Ⓒ. 8

    B. 7   D. 9

8. How many sections of a shape would you shade to represent **15%** if the shape was divided into **60** equal parts?

    A. 7   C. 9

    Ⓑ. 8   D. 10

9. How many sections of a shape would you shade to represent 10% if the shape was divided into 20 equal parts?

A. 1   C. 3
B. 2   D. 4

10. How many sections of a shape would you shade to represent 50% if the shape was divided into 42 equal parts?

A. 21   C. 22
B. 20   D. 24

11. Sydney is making cookies. The recipe calls for 3 eggs for each batch of 24 cookies. If she has 15 eggs, how many cookies can she make?

A. 105   C. 115
B. 110   D. 120

12. Max makes trail mix for his boy scout troop. He uses 4 cups of nuts and 1 cup of candy. If his container can hold 25 cups, how many cups of nuts does he need to include?

A. 16   C. 20
B. 15   D. 25

13. Shannon is mixing paint to paint her room purple. She uses 3 gallons of red paint and 5 gallons of blue paint. If she needs 24 gallons to paint her room, how much blue paint does she need?

A. 3   C. 10
B. 5   D. 15

14. Matt makes lemonade using 3 quarts of water and one quart of lemon juice. If he has a container that holds 12 quarts how much lemon juice does he need?

A. 4 quarts   C. 2 quarts
B. 1 quart   D. 3 quarts

15. Melissa makes hot tea. She uses 2 teaspoons of milk for each cup of tea. If she has 30 teaspoons of milk, how many cups of tea can she make?

A. 10   C. 20
B. 15   D. 25

fitness

Please be aware of your environment and be safe at all times. If you cannot do an exercise, just try your best.

Repeat these exercises 4 ROUNDS

1 - High Plank: 25 sec.

2 - Chair: 20 sec.
Note: sit on an imaginary chair, keep your back straight.

3 - Waist Hooping: 20 times. Note: if you do not have a hoop, pretend you have an imaginary hoop and rotate your hips 10 times.

4 - Abs: 25 times

Ratios and Percents

Use the information below to answer today's questions.

1 inch= 2.54 cm
1 foot= 30.48 cm
3.28 feet= 1 meter
1 mile= 1.61 kilometers
0.035 ounces= 1 gram
2.21 pounds= 1 kilogram
1 teaspoon= 4.92 milliliters
0.68 tablespoons= 10 milliliters

1. How many inches are in 4.6 cm?

    A. 1.8 inches
    B. 0.8 inches
    C. 2.8 inches
    D. 2.4 inches

2. How many miles are in 7 km?

    A. 4.1 miles
    B. 4.3 miles
    C. 4.5 miles
    D. 4.7 miles

3. How many milliliters are in 14 tablespoons?

    A. 198
    B. 202
    C. 206
    D. 210

4. How many feet are in 21 meters?

    A. 63   C. 67
    B. 65   D. 69

5. About how many pounds are in 16 kilograms?

    A. 32
    B. 33
    C. 34
    D. 35

6. About how many feet are in 83 centimeters?

    A. 3
    B. 4
    C. 5
    D. 6

7. About how many kilometers are in 6.5 miles?

    A. 10.5
    B. 11
    C. 11.5
    D. 12

8. How many ounces are in 64 grams?

    A. 2.14
    B. 2.24
    C. 2.34
    D. 2.44

9. How many teaspoons are in 28 milliliters?

    A. 5.3
    B. 5.5
    C. 5.7
    D. 5.9

10. About how many kilograms are in 16 pounds?

A. 4
B. 5
C. 6
D. 7

11. It takes 32 miles to get to a new amusement park. About how far away is the park in kilometers?

A. 46
B. 48
C. 50
D. 52

12. The town pond is 18 inches deep. About how deep is the lake in centimeters?

A. 42
B. 44
C. 46
D. 48

13. Maggie buys a bike that is 152.9 cm high. About how high is bike in feet?

A. 5
B. 6
C. 7
D. 8

14. Travis's backpack is 8 pounds. How heavy is it in kilograms?

A. 3.6
B. 3.8
C. 4
D. 4.2

15. Sam's doctor tells him to take 2 teaspoons a day of his medicine. How many milliliters of medicine does he need to take every day?

A. 9.48
B. 9.84
C. 8.94
D. 8.49

yoga

Please be aware of your environment and be safe at all times. If you cannot do an exercise, just try your best.

1 - Down Dog: 30 sec.

2 - Bend Down: 30 sec.

3 - Chair: 30 sec.

4 - Child Pose: 30 sec.

5 - Shavasana: as long as you can. Note: think of happy moments and relax your mind.

Tracking Populations

Last week, we introduced the word **population** as "a group of organisms (animals or plants) who are the <u>same species</u> and live in the <u>same area</u>." Over the next few days, you'll do your best to try and figure out what **populations** of different animals live in your area and which **populations** are the biggest. Conservationists, park rangers, fish and game wardens, and other environmental professionals do this kind of work frequently to help understand how many different kinds of animals live in the wild.

NOTE: This activity is done over the course of a few days and requires some outdoor work, so be sure you start on a day with good weather.

Materials:

- Notepaper
- Plain white paper
- Art supplies (colored pencils, markers, etc.)
- A safe outdoor space (such as a large back yard or public park) that you can easily access multiple times over the course of a week
- Local Bird/Wildlife identification books (available at your local library)
- Binoculars (optional)

Procedure:

1. Before you begin this activity, visit your local library and check out one or two books about birds and animals that are native to your local area. You also might be able to find relevant information on your state's Department of Fish and Game or Department of Fish and Wildlife website.

2. Find a safe outdoor space that you can visit for each of the next five days. If you have a large yard, you can use that space, or you can use a neighborhood park or hiking trail.

3. On your first day, bring your notepaper and binoculars (if you have them) with you to your safe outdoor space and find a place where you can sit or stand comfortably for 15-20 minutes. Try to be as quiet as possible as you look and listen for animals. The first time you see an animal or bird, make a quick note of what it is on your notepaper (for example, if you saw a squirrel, you could just write "squirrel"). If you're not sure what kind of animal or bird it is, try to write down a quick description (like "small, red bird with black legs"). If you see another of the same animal again, make a check or tally mark to keep track of how many of each species of bird or animal you're seeing.

4. After you've observed animals and birds for 15-20 minutes, return home.

5. Create a "master note sheet" so that you can document which animals or birds you saw each day (this will be easier and neater than trying to bring the same note sheet outside every day). Transfer your findings to the paper and use your art supplies to draw a picture of each animal or bird as well. Use this time to look up any animals you had trouble identifying in your books from the library or using reputable online resources.

6. Repeat this process for five days, visiting the same spot for 15-20 minutes and writing down which animals or birds you see and how many of each you observe. After your daily trip, upload your findings to your master note sheet.

7. After five days, study your master sheet and see: How many **different** kinds of animals did you see? Which animals and birds were **most common?** Which animals are birds were rare but visible? Which other animals did your resources suggest should have been around **that you didn't see?**

8. Once you've completed this activity, save your master note sheet, as you will need it next week.

experiment

Follow-Up Questions:

1. Based on your study, what are the **three** most thriving and noticeable animal populations in the space you observed?

_____

_____

_____

2. Based on the books you checked out or online resources you used, were your findings **different from what you expected?** Were there any animals you thought you'd see more or less of?

_____

_____

_____

yoga

Please be aware of your environment and be safe at all times. If you cannot do an exercise, just try your best.

3 - Stretching: Stay as long as possible. Note: do on one leg then on another.

2 - Down Dog: 30 sec.

4 - Lower Plank: 20 sec. Note: Keep your back straight and body tight.

1 - Tree Pose: Stay as long as possible. Note: do on one leg then on another.

6 - Shavasana: 5 min. Note: this pose is very important and provides you with long term benefits. Try not to skip this. Close your eyes and imagine who you want to be and what your goals are! Always think happy thoughts.

5 - Book Pose: 20 sec. Note: Keep your core tight. Legs should be across from your eyes.

MaZe

Task: Start on the left entrance and work your way through the maze to exit on the right.

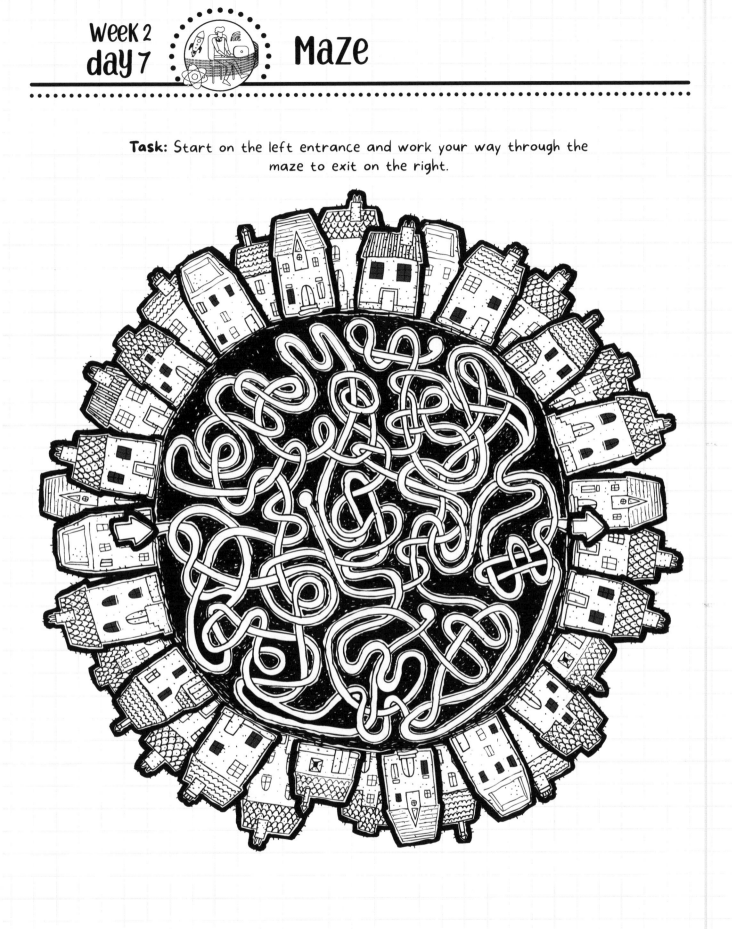

Explaining Relationships Between Ideas

Over the last two weeks, you've discovered some tools and strategies to help you read texts closely, one sentence at a time. Like we said last week, reading this way is great because it ensures that you understand the text at every level. This week, we'll deepen our close reading skills by thinking more about **relationships between ideas**.

As you read increasingly complex texts, you'll be presented with more and more **ideas**. One of your most important jobs as a reader is to understand not just each idea on its own but also how various different ideas connect, influence, and contribute to one another. When you're able to explain relationships between ideas, you're truly showing that you comprehend a text and can apply your own thinking and analysis to it.

In Informational Texts:
When you're reading **nonfiction** or **informational texts**, it's crucial to follow the main ideas that are laid out and understand the connections between them. Generally, it's **impossible** to have a complete understanding of an informational text without exploring how its different points and parts work together. As you read an **informational text**, ask yourself...
- What are **the main ideas**? (Long texts contain tons of ideas. Your first job is to pick out the truly important ones. Otherwise, it's hard to know where to focus!)
- **Why** did the author present these ideas **in this order**? (Would things feel or read significantly different if they were presented in an alternate order? Is the order essential to clarity of ideas?)
- How are the ideas from different paragraphs, sections, chapters, etc. **connected** or **similar**?
- How are ideas from different paragraphs, sections, chapters, etc. **disconnected or different**? (If you're noticing a lot of **disconnected** ideas, the text you're reading might not be very strong!)

In Literary Texts:
When you're reading **fiction** or another kind of **literary text**, you need to think about **plot**, **character, and setting** in terms of relationships. For example...
- How does an event in the **plot** lead to the next event? Why do things happen the way they do?
  - This often has to do with **cause-and-effect** relationships
- How do the **character's actions** impact the plot?
- How do the **character's inner feelings and personalities** connect to (or differ from) the events being depicted in the story?
- How are the different **settings** (locations) where the story takes place similar or different? How do they create different **tones or moods** for the scenes or events that take place there?

From "Walden"

By Henry David Thoreau

(Continued from Week 2's Passage. This part of "Walden" focuses on some of the sounds Thoreau experienced while he lived in the woods.)

Some of my pleasantest hours were during the long rain storms in the spring or fall, which confined me to the house for the afternoon as well as the forenoon, soothed by their ceaseless roar and pelting; when an early twilight ushered in a long evening in which many thoughts had time to take root and unfold themselves. In those driving north-east rains which tried the village houses so, when the maids stood ready with mop and pail in front entries to keep the deluge out, I sat behind my door in my little house, which was all entry, and thoroughly enjoyed its protection. In one heavy thunder shower the lightning struck a large pitch-pine across the pond, making a very conspicuous and perfectly regular spiral groove from top to bottom, an inch or more deep, and four or five inches wide, as you would groove a walking-stick. I passed it again the other day, and was struck with awe on looking up and beholding that mark, now more distinct than ever, where a terrific and resistless bolt came down out of the harmless sky eight years ago.

Men frequently say to me, "I should think you would feel lonesome down there, and want to be nearer to folks, rainy and snowy days and nights especially." I am tempted to reply to such, — This whole earth which we inhabit is but a point in space. How far apart, think you, dwell the two most distant inhabitants of yonder star, the breadth of whose disk cannot be appreciated by our instruments? Why should I feel lonely? is not our planet in the Milky Way? This which you put seems to me not to be the most important question. What sort of space is that which separates a man from his fellows and makes him solitary? I have found that no exertion of the legs can bring two minds much nearer to one another. What do we want most to dwell near to? Not to many men surely, the depot, the post-office, the bar-room, the meeting-house, the school-house, the grocery, Beacon Hill, or the Five Points, where men most congregate, but to the perennial source of our life, whence in all our experience we have found that to issue, as the willow stands near the water and sends out its roots in that direction. This will vary with different natures, but this is the place where a wise man will dig his cellar.

1. How does Thoreau **contrast** his experience of rain storms to the way they are experienced in the village?

_____

_____

_____

2. Why does Thoreau become interested in the **pitch-pine** across the pond from his cabin?

_____

_____

_____

3. Who are "the two most distant inhabitants of yonder star" mentioned in the passages?

   A. Thoreau and the man who asked him if he feels lonesome
   B. Aliens who might live very far away
   C. The people who congregate in Five Points
   D. The people who control rain and lightning

4. What does Thoreau mean when he writes, "I have found that no exertion of the legs can bring two minds much nearer to one another"?

   A. You can't just run away from your problems.
   B. Being part of the community is more important than anything else.
   C. It's impossible to get closer to people who aren't like you.
   D. It doesn't matter if you are physically close to people if you don't feel connected to them.

5. In this passage, Thoreau talks a lot about the idea of **community** and social **interaction**. How important do you think being **social** and interacting with other people on a regular basis is? Do you prefer to be social or spend time alone thinking? Explain your choice.

_____

_____

_____

_____

_____

Explaining Relationships Between Ideas

Directions: Review each set of related ideas below. Then, write an **explanation** using <u>your own words</u> that communicates the exact **relationship** between those two ideas. Imagine you are writing a single sentence with the goal to make things as clear as possible for the reader.

1. **IDEA 1:** Brushing and flossing your teeth
    IDEA 2: Cavities are painful and unpleasant to fill

    In your own words, how are these ideas connected?

    _____

    _____

    _____

2. **IDEA 1:** I always hit the snooze button on my alarm clock two or three times
    IDEA 2: I have gotten two detentions this year for lateness

    In your own words, how are these ideas connected?

    _____

    _____

    _____

3. **IDEA 1:** My older sister dented our mother's car
    IDEA 2: My older sister has only been driving for six months

    In your own words, how are these ideas connected?

    _____

    _____

    _____

4. **IDEA 1:** Our last field trip got cancelled because so many people were failing math
    IDEA 2: Our next field trip is scheduled for right after report cards come out.

    In your own words, how are these ideas connected?

_____

_____

_____

fitness

Please be aware of your environment and be safe at all times. If you cannot do an exercise, just try your best.

Repeat these **exercises 4 ROUNDS**

2 - Lunges: 8 times to each leg. Note: Use your body weight or books as weight to do leg lunges.

1 - Abs: 20 times

3 - Plank: 20 sec.

4 - Run: 50m Note: Run 25 meters to one side and 25 meters back to the starting position.

From "Walden"

By Henry David Thoreau

(Continued from Day 1's Passage)

Society is commonly too cheap. We meet at very short intervals, not having had time to acquire any new value for each other. We meet at meals three times a day, and give each other a new taste of that old musty cheese that we are. We have had to agree on a certain set of rules, called etiquette and politeness, to make this frequent meeting tolerable and that we need not come to open war. We meet at the post-office, and at the sociable, and about the fireside every night; we live thick and are in each other's way, and stumble over one another, and I think that we thus lose some respect for one another. Certainly less frequency would suffice for all important and hearty communications. Consider the girls in a factory ,— never alone, hardly in their dreams. It would be better if there were but one inhabitant to a square mile, as where I live. The value of a man is not in his skin, that we should touch him.

I have heard of a man lost in the woods and dying of famine and exhaustion at the foot of a tree, whose loneliness was relieved by the grotesque visions with which, owing to bodily weakness, his diseased imagination surrounded him, and which he believed to be real. So also, owing to bodily and mental health and strength, we may be continually cheered by a like but more normal and natural society, and come to know that we are never alone.

I have a great deal of company in my house; especially in the morning, when nobody calls. Let me suggest a few comparisons, that some one may convey an idea of my situation. I am no more lonely than the loon in the pond that laughs so loud, or than Walden Pond itself. What company has that lonely lake, I pray? And yet it has not the blue devils, but the blue angels in it, in the azure tint of its waters. The sun is alone, except in thick weather, when there sometimes appear to be two, but one is a mock sun. I am no more lonely than a single mullein or dandelion in a pasture, or a bean leaf, or sorrel, or a horse-fly, or a bumble-bee. I am no more lonely than the Mill Brook, or a weathercock, or the north star, or the south wind, or an April shower, or a January thaw, or the first spider in a new house.

1. How do the ideas **at the beginning** of this passage connect to the ideas from Day 1's passage?

_____

_____

_____

_____

2. Based on Paragraph 1, what does Thoreau think is silly, stupid, or unnecessary about **society**?

_____

_____

_____

_____

3. Which of these best represents the **main idea** of Paragraph 2?

    A. When people spend time alone, their brain and imagination are capable of incredible things.

    B. Being alone can be incredibly scary, especially if you are sick or hurt.

    C. People's imaginations tend to go to the dark side when they are alone.

    D. If you're going to live alone, you must stay physically and mentally healthy.

4. What is the connection between Paragraph 2 and Paragraph 3?

    A. In Paragraph 2, Thoreau provides an example from his own situation. Then, in Paragraph 3, he applies that thinking to an abstract idea.

    B. In Paragraph 2, Thoreau introduces an idea abstractly. Then, in Paragraph 3, he applies that idea to his own situation.

    C. In Paragraph 2, Thoreau discusses a person without mentioning their name. In Paragraph 3, Thoreau reveals that that person is actually him.

    D. In Paragraph 2, Thoreau discusses an area without mentioning its name. In Paragraph 3, Thoreau reveals that area is actually Walden Pond.

5. Based on Paragraph 3, why does Thoreau say that he is **not** lonely living by himself?

_____

_____

_____

Explaining Relationships Between Ideas in a Text

Directions: Review each set of related ideas below. All these ideas are drawn from the Day 2 reading passage, so you may want to **refer back to the text** as you think about and consider each pair of ideas. Then, write an **explanation** using your own words that communicates the exact **relationship** between those two ideas. Imagine you are writing a single sentence with the goal to make things as clear as possible for the reader.

1. **IDEA 1:** "Society is commonly too cheap."
   IDEA 2: "We have had to agree on a certain set of rules, called etiquette and politeness, to make this frequent meeting tolerable and that we need not come to open war."
   (**NOTE:** These lines come from Paragraph 1)

   In your own words, how are these ideas connected?

   _____

   _____

   _____

2. **IDEA 1:** "I have heard of a man lost in the woods and dying of famine and exhaustion at the foot of a tree, whose loneliness was relieved by the grotesque visions with which, owing to bodily weakness, his diseased imagination surrounded him..."
   IDEA 2: "[W]e may be continually cheered by a like but more normal and natural society, and come to know that we are never alone."
   (**NOTE:** These lines come from Paragraph 2)

   In your own words, how are these ideas connected?

   _____

   _____

   _____

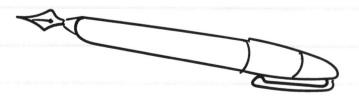

3. **IDEA 1:** "I have a great deal of company in my house; especially in the morning..."
    IDEA 2: "What company has that lonely lake, I pray?"
    (**NOTE:** These lines come from Paragraph 3)

    In your own words, how are these ideas connected?

    _____

    _____

    _____

fitness

Please be aware of your environment and be safe at all times. If you cannot do an exercise, just try your best.

Repeat these **exercises 4 ROUNDS**

2 - Side Bending: 15 times to each side. Note: try to touch your feet.

1 - Squats: 20 times. Note: imagine you are trying to sit on a chair.

3 - Tree Pose: Stay as long as possible. Note: do the same with the other leg.

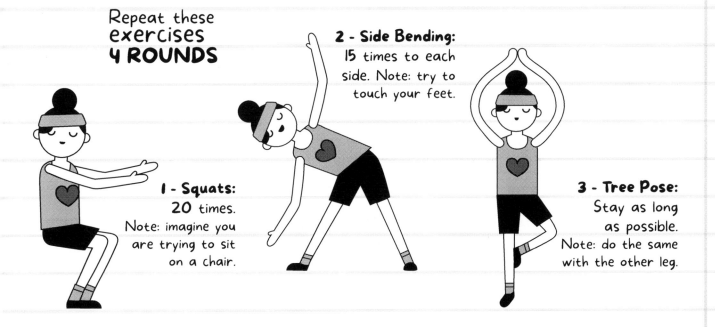

Number Systems

1. $\frac{1}{2} \div 1\frac{1}{4}$

   A. $\frac{2}{5}$ C. $\frac{1}{8}$

   B. $\frac{5}{2}$ D. $\frac{3}{8}$

2. $\frac{3}{2} \div 1\frac{3}{7}$

   A. $\frac{2}{3}$ C. $\frac{21}{20}$

   B. $\frac{4}{5}$ D. $\frac{20}{21}$

3. $\frac{14}{5} \div 2$

   A. $\frac{8}{10}$ C. $\frac{12}{10}$

   B. $\frac{14}{10}$ D. $\frac{6}{10}$

4. $\frac{1}{9} \div 1\frac{1}{3}$

   A. $\frac{1}{6}$ C. $\frac{1}{10}$

   B. $\frac{1}{8}$ D. $\frac{1}{12}$

5. $\frac{1}{2} \div 1\frac{1}{7}$

   A. $\frac{1}{7}$ C. $\frac{5}{17}$

   B. $\frac{3}{17}$ D. $\frac{7}{16}$

6. $8 \div \frac{2}{3}$

   A. 12   C. $\frac{1}{12}$

   B. 24   D. $\frac{1}{24}$

7. $6 \div \frac{4}{7}$

   A. $3\frac{2}{7}$ C. $10\frac{1}{2}$

   B. $4\frac{3}{2}$ D. $9\frac{1}{2}$

8. $3 \div \frac{2}{9}$

   A. $12\frac{1}{3}$ C. $3\frac{1}{2}$

   B. $13\frac{1}{2}$ D. $9\frac{2}{3}$

9. $2 \div \frac{1}{8}$

   A. 16   C. $\frac{1}{16}$

   B. 4   D. $\frac{1}{4}$

10. $7 \div \frac{3}{5}$

    A. $7\frac{3}{5}$ C. $10\frac{1}{3}$

    B. $9\frac{1}{5}$ D. $11\frac{2}{3}$

MatH

11. $\frac{1}{7} \div \frac{2}{4}$

   A. $\frac{7}{2}$ C. $\frac{1}{2}$

   B. $\frac{2}{7}$ D. $\frac{1}{7}$

12. $\frac{3}{9} \div \frac{1}{2}$

   A. $\frac{6}{9}$ C. $\frac{2}{6}$

   B. $\frac{4}{9}$ D. $\frac{7}{9}$

13. $\frac{5}{8} \div \frac{6}{7}$

   A. $\frac{7}{8}$ C. $\frac{35}{48}$

   B. $\frac{35}{45}$ D. $\frac{30}{48}$

14. $\frac{2}{3} \div \frac{9}{8}$

   A. $\frac{18}{32}$ C. $\frac{17}{26}$

   B. $\frac{14}{20}$ D. $\frac{16}{27}$

15. $\frac{1}{4} \div \frac{5}{6}$

   A. $\frac{6}{26}$ C. $\frac{3}{10}$

   B. $\frac{6}{10}$ D. $\frac{3}{20}$

fitness

Please be aware of your environment and be safe at all times. If you cannot do an exercise, just try your best.

Repeat these **exercises 4 ROUNDS**

2 - Lunges: 12 times to each leg.
Note: Use your body weight or books as weight to do leg lunges.

3 - Plank: 20 sec.

1 - Bend forward: 15 times.
Note: try to touch your feet. Make sure to keep your back straight and if needed you can bend your knees.

4 - Abs: 20 times

Number Systems

1. 1755 ÷ 65

   A. 25   C. 27
   B. 26   D. 28

2. 1596 ÷ 38

   A. 40   C. 44
   B. 42   D. 46

3. 583 ÷ 53

   A. 8   C. 10
   B. 9   D. 11

4. 651 ÷ 21

   A. 31   C. 33
   B. 32   D. 34

5. 915 ÷ 61

   A. 15   C. 17
   B. 16   D. 18

6. 5319 ÷ 18

   A. 281 R3
   B. 296 R2
   C. 295 R9
   D. 304

7. 1472 ÷ 22

   A. 68 R3
   B. 26 R20
   C. 65 R21
   D. 66 R20

8. 8729 ÷ 38

   A. 228 R20
   B. 229 R27
   C. 229 R14
   D. 230 R2

9. 1791 ÷ 45

   A. 36 R39
   B. 39 R36
   C. 28 R32
   D. 45 R47

10. 6198 ÷ 86

    A. 71 R6
    B. 72 R6
    C. 72 R23
    D. 73 R6

11. A relay race covers 3 miles and each teammate will run $\frac{3}{4}$ of a mile. How many runners are needed for the race?

    A. 3   C. 4
    B. 2   D. 6

MatH

12. Laura is painting furniture. She has $\frac{2}{3}$ of a liter of paint remaining. Each piece of furniture requires $\frac{4}{15}$ of a liter of paint. How many pieces of furniture can she paint?

A. 4   C. 1
B. 3   D. 2

13. A benefit concert wants to make at least $3,500. If they plan to charge $45 per ticket, how many tickets do they need to sell?

A. 78
B. 77
C. 76
D. 75

14. Our school is going on a field trip. There are 638 total students going on the trip. If each bus carries 42 students, how many buses are needed?

A. 15
B. 16
C. 17
D. 18

15. Our town has $8,325 to clean the public areas. If they plan on paying 15 people $15 an hour for the work, how many hours will each person need to work?

A. 35
B. 36
C. 37
D. 38

fitness

Please be aware of your environment and be safe at all times. If you cannot do an exercise, just try your best.

Repeat these **exercises 4 ROUNDS**

2 - Chair: 20 sec.
Note: sit on an imaginary chair, keep your back straight.

4 - Abs: 25 times

1 - High Plank: 25 sec.

3 - Waist Hooping: 20 times. Note: if you do not have a hoop, pretend you have an imaginary hoop and rotate your hips 10 times.

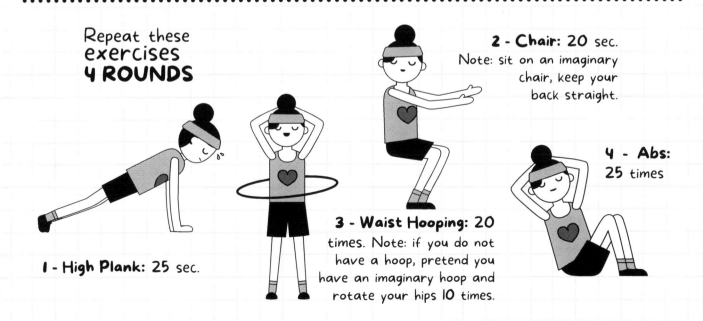

Number Systems

1. 0.472 + 7.127

A. 8.427
B. 4.877
C. 7.487
D. 7.599

2. 4.179 + 9.128

A. 10.037
B. 31.703
C. 13.307
D. 13.137

3. 15 - 8.269

A. 6.731
B. 6.127
C. 6.317
D. 6.137

4. 73.127 - 38.756

A. 32.731
B. 34.371
C. 37.713
D. 33.771

5. 9.127 x 8.23

A. 75.51122
B. 75
C. 75.11
D. 75.11521

6. 0.194 x 2.12

A. 41.128
B. 0.28
C. 0.41128
D. 0.411

7. 26.5328 ÷ 3.68

A. 7.21
B. 2.17
C. 7.18
D. 7.23

8. 58.5 ÷ 0.65

A. 75
B. 80
C. 85
D. 90

9. What is the greatest common factor of 9, 24, and 42?

A. 12
B. 9
C. 6
D. 3

10. What is the greatest common factor of 12 and 84?

A. 12
B. 2
C. 4
D. 3

11. What is the greatest common factor of 60 and 45?

A. 15
B. 5
C. 6
D. 9

12. What is the least common multiple of 12 and 18?

A. 34
B. 36
C. 38
D. 216

13. What is the least common multiple of 10 and 6?

A. 15
B. 20
C. 30
D. 60

14. What is the least common multiple of 2 and 14?

A. 12
B. 14
C. 16
D. 18

15. Emily is planting a small flower garden and herb garden. One garden is 42 inches wide and the other garden is 28 inches wide. If she wants the plants to be equally and evenly spaced in both gardens, how much inches of space should she put between the plants?

A. 8
B. 10
C. 12
D. 14

 yoGa

Please be aware of your environment and be safe at all times. If you cannot do an exercise, just try your best.

1 - Down Dog: 30 sec.

2 - Bend Down: 30 sec.

3 - Chair: 30 sec.

4 - Child Pose: 30 sec.

5 - Shavasana: as long as you can. Note: think of happy moments and relax your mind.

Biodiversity

During last week's activities you got a sense of the **biodiversity** in your area by studying the **populations** of local birds and animals. This week, we'll do an activity that extends that thinking to include **plants** as well. Plants are key to biodiversity because they provide food and shelter for many of the different animals, birds, and insects you saw last week.

This week, you'll be visiting an outdoor space to observe local plant life.

Materials:

- Notepaper
- A safe outdoor space (ideally a wilder space rather than a landscaped one)
- A digital camera (a cell phone camera works perfectly)
- Local plant/botany books (available at your local library)
- Art supplies (optional)
- Plain white paper (optional)

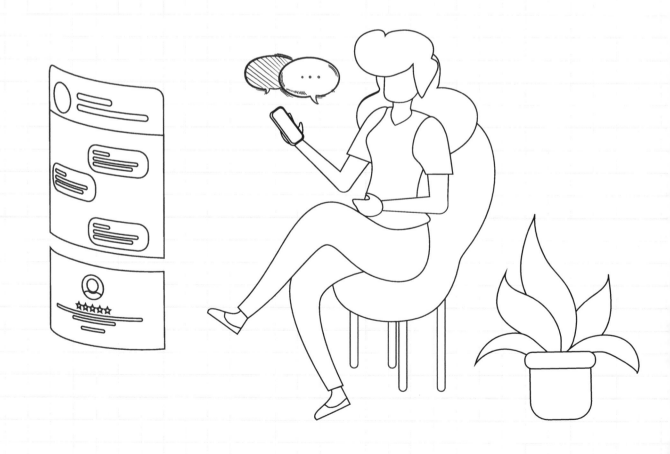

Procedure:

1. Before you begin this investigation, stop by your local library and take out one or two books on plant life in your local area (these will probably be near where you found the wildlife books last week).

2. Find a safe outdoor space that contains wild plant life. If the place you used last week fits that criteria, then feel free to use it again. If you used a landscaped area (like a backyard or playground) last week, you will want to find something wilder that will help you understand which plants are actively native to your area. Bring your digital camera with you.

3. Walk around your safe outdoor space for 15-20 minutes and see how many different types of plants and trees you can find. Using your digital camera, take pictures of each different type of plant or tree. If you like to draw, you can bring art supplies and draw them as well.

4. After you've photographed as many different trees and plants as possible in your safe outdoor space, return home.

5. Look at your photographs and, using your local plant/botany books from the library (and other online resources that might be available through your state's Department of Agriculture), do your best to identify each different type of tree or plant. On your note sheet, write down the names of each different type of tree or plant and a few notes about their appearance or how common they were in the area you observed.

6. Once you've identified all the different plants/trees, take out your master note sheet from last week and compare the two documents. Consider how the animals in your area might use the trees/plants you saw, and answer the questions below.

experiment

Follow-Up Questions:

1. How do the plants/trees you saw in a **wilder** outdoor space <u>**differ**</u> from the plants/trees that people typically have in **landscaped** yards?

_____

_____

_____

2. What are some different ways **the animals you observed last week** might use or have relationships with the **plants/trees you observed in this activity?**

_____

_____

_____

yoga

Please be aware of your environment and be safe at all times. If you cannot do an exercise, just try your best.

3 - Stretching: Stay as long as possible. Note: do on one leg then on another.

2 - Down Dog: 30 sec.

4 - Lower Plank: 20 sec. Note: Keep your back straight and body tight.

1 - Tree Pose: Stay as long as possible. Note: do on one leg then on another.

6 - Shavasana: 5 min. Note: this pose is very important and provides you with long term benefits. Try not to skip this. Close your eyes and imagine who you want to be and what your goals are! Always think happy thoughts.

5 - Book Pose: 20 sec. Note: Keep your core tight. Legs should be across from your eyes.

Task: Using the stairs and ladders, find the way from point 1 to point 2.
Do not jump or climb up!

73

WeeK 4

OVERVIEW OF ENGLISH CONCEPTS

Identifying Word Relationships

So far this summer, we've been focusing on close reading skills. We've looked at ways to examine a text **one sentence at a time** to build a <u>strong comprehension</u> of textual meaning and help us <u>understand the relationships between ideas</u>. Today, we'll look at some key "watch words" to keep an eye out for as you read. These words signify important relationships, sequences, and organizational structures that directly impact the meaning of sentences, both individually and as a whole.

Noticing word relationships within a sentence can speed up the comprehension process and help you recognize terminology and sentence structure that may be repeated later on in the text. As a writer, understanding word relationships helps you craft strong, interesting sentences that can access ideas a variety of different ways.

<u>**Examples of Sets of Words with Important Relationships:**</u>

Word 1: Cause
Word 2: Effect
Relationship: The first thing directly caused the second thing to happen

Word 1: Part
Word 2: Whole
Relationship: The first thing is simply one aspect or element of a greater, larger idea (the whole).

Word 1: Item
Word 2: Category
Relationship: Much like **part and whole**, an **item** is one idea, object, or person, whereas a category could contain many similar ideas that have been grouped together

Word 1: Primary
Word 2: Other
Relationship: The **primary** reason or idea is the main or most important concept. Anything else is less important. (If the author uses words like **"secondary" or "tertiary,"** you can actually rank the importance of ideas numerically!)

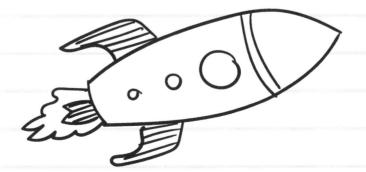

As a Reader:

As we've said before, it's crucial to understand each sentence within a text to have a complete understanding. As you read, it can be useful to **underline or circle words** that signify important relationships (like the ones above and many others). That way, when you summarize or check for comprehension, you can scan those words visually to double-check your understanding of the relationships between ideas.

As a Writer:

Always use the best possible words to make things clear and easy-to-understand for the reader. As you continue to get older and grow in experience as a reader and writer, watch how your favorite authors and writers use words to communicate meaning. There's nothing wrong with "borrowing" the terminology and structure that they use to create organization and clarity in their writing!

From "Oliver Twist"

By Charles Dickens

Among other public buildings in a certain town which for many reasons it will be prudent to refrain from mentioning, and to which I will assign no fictitious name, it boasts of one which is common to most towns, great or small, to wit, a workhouse; and in this workhouse was born, on a day and date which I need not take upon myself to repeat, inasmuch as it can be of no possible consequence to the reader, in this stage of the business at all events, the item of mortality whose name is prefixed to the head of this story. For a long time after he was ushered into this world of sorrow and trouble, by the parish surgeon, it remained a matter of considerable doubt whether the child would survive to bear any name at all; in which case it is somewhat more than probable that these memoirs would never have appeared, or, if they had, being comprised within a couple of pages, that they would have possessed the inestimable merit of being the most concise and faithful specimen of biography extant in the literature of any age or country.

Although I am not disposed to maintain that the being born in a workhouse is in itself the most fortunate and enviable circumstance that can possibly befall a human being, I do mean to say that in this particular instance it was the best thing for Oliver Twist that could by possibility have occurred. The fact is, that there was considerable difficulty in inducing Oliver to take upon himself the job of breathing, — a troublesome practice, but one which custom has rendered necessary to our easy existence, — and for some time he lay gasping on a little flock mattress, rather unequally poised between this world and the next, the balance being decidedly in favor of the latter.

Now, if during this brief period, Oliver had been surrounded by careful grandmothers, anxious aunts, experienced nurses, and doctors of profound wisdom, he would most inevitably and indubitably have been killed in no time. There being nobody by, however, but a poor old woman, who was rendered rather misty by an unwonted allowance of beer, and a parish surgeon who did such matters by contract, Oliver and nature fought out the point between them. The result was, that, after a few struggles, Oliver breathed, sneezed, and proceeded to advertise to the inmates of the workhouse the fact of a new burden having been imposed upon the parish.

1. Why does the author **not** name the **town** or **neighborhood** where the story takes place in Paragraph 1?

_____

_____

_____

2. What clues or ideas from this passage communicate that Oliver is born **poor** and with **very little**?

_____

_____

_____

_____

3. Who or what is the **"item of mortality"** described in Paragraph 1?

   A. The workhouse
   B. Oliver Twist
   C. The poor old woman
   D. The parish surgeon

4. What **problem** is Oliver born with?

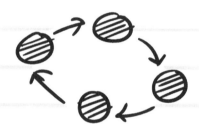

   A. He cannot see.
   B. He cannot hear.
   C. He cannot breathe.
   D. He cries whenever anybody touches him.

5. Based on the **tone** and **content** of this passage, <u>make a prediction</u> as to what kind of life you think Oliver Twist is likely to have after being born this way. What makes you think that's what's going to happen?

_____

_____

_____

_____

_____

Identifying Word Relationships (Pt. 1)

Directions: Read each sentence below and think about the **relationships between words** as you read. Answer the question that follows each sentence to focus on specific concepts that can only be understood if you grasp the relationships between words.

1. If a paragraph begins:
    "One of the main causes of the Civil War was the difference in economic model between North and South."
    ...which of these statements is **definitely** true?

    A. Difference in economic model caused the Civil War.
    B. Difference in economic model was one of many factors that caused the Civil War.
    C. Difference in economic model was one of the most important factors that caused the Civil War.
    D. Difference in economic model was the most important factor that caused the Civil War.

2. If a sentence states:
    "Among dogs, terriers like the West Highland White, Soft Coated Wheaten, and Bull Terrier have some of the strongest and most tenacious personalities."
    ...which of these statements is **not** true?

    A. Soft Coated Wheatens are an example of terriers.
    B. West Highland Whites are an example of dogs.
    C. Bull Terriers and West Highland Whites are both examples of terriers.
    D. "Dog" and "terrier" are synonyms.

3. If a paragraph begins:
"Lowering property taxes would be a major benefit to our town."
...which of these statements would likely **not** fit in that paragraph?

A. Our current tax rate has allowed the town to build a new community center and improve public parks.

B. With reduced tax burden, town residents would be empowered to invest money in home improvements.

C. Increased spending money would allow town residents to support local businesses better.

D. More young families would be likely to move to our town if taxes were lower.

fitness

Please be aware of your environment and be safe at all times. If you cannot do an exercise, just try your best.

Repeat these **exercises 4 ROUNDS**

2 - Lunges: 8 times to each leg. Note: Use your body weight or books as weight to do leg lunges.

1 - Abs: 20 times

3 - Plank: 20 sec.

4 - Run: 50m Note: Run 25 meters to one side and 25 meters back to the starting position.

From "Oliver Twist"

By Charles Dickens

For the next eight or ten months, Oliver was the victim of a systematic course of treachery and deception — he was brought up by hand. The hungry and destitute situation of the infant orphan was duly reported by the workhouse authorities to the parish authorities. The parish authorities inquired with dignity of the workhouse authorities, whether there was no female then domiciled in "the house" who was in a situation to impart to Oliver Twist the consolation and nourishment of which he stood in need. The workhouse authorities replied with humility that there was not. Upon this, the parish authorities magnanimously and humanely resolved, that Oliver should be "farmed," or, in other words, that he should be dispatched to a branch-workhouse some three miles off, where twenty or thirty other juvenile offenders against the poor-laws rolled about the floor all day, without the inconvenience of too much food or too much clothing, under the parental superintendence of an elderly female who received the culprits at and for the consideration of sevenpence-halfpenny per small head per week. Sevenpence-halfpenny's worth per week is a good round diet for a child; a great deal may be got for for sevenpence-halfpenny—quite enough to overload its stomach, and make it uncomfortable. The elderly female was a woman of wisdom and experience; she knew what was good for children, and she had a very accurate perception of what was good for herself. So, she appropriated the greater part of the weekly stipend to her own use, and consigned the rising parochial generation to even a shorter allowance than was originally provided for them; thereby finding in the lowest depth a deeper still, and proving herself a very great experimental philosopher...

Unfortunately for the experimental philosophy of the female to whose protecting care Oliver Twist was delivered over, a negative result usually attended the operation of her system; for at the very moment when a child had contrived to exist upon the smallest possible portion of the weakest possible food, it did perversely happen in eight and a half cases out of ten, either that it sickened from want and cold, or fell into the fire from neglect, or got smothered by accident; in any one of which cases, the miserable little being was usually summoned into another world, and there gathered to the fathers which it had never known in this.

1. Describe the "**elderly female**" with whom Oliver is sent to live with in your **own words**:

    _____

    _____

2. Why is it especially tragic that the parish sends the elderly female "sevenpence-halfpenny" each week for every child in her care?

    _____

    _____

3. What is the main reason **Oliver** cannot continue to live in the **main workhouse**?

    A. He is a child.
    B. He is naughty and disobedient.
    C. They do not have money to care for him.
    D. There is nobody there who can nurse him.

4. **Why** do children who live with the "elderly female" often die?

    A. The children are rough, juvenile delinquents who often get into fights.
    B. She feeds and cares for them as little as possible.
    C. She is actually a witch.
    D. She is too old and weak to protect them herself.

5. **Why** do you think Dickens begins his book by showing what a hard, sad childhood the main character had?

    _____

    _____

    _____

    _____

Identifying Word Relationships (Pt. 2)

Directions: Read each sentence below and think about the **relationships between words** as you read. **All these sentences have been taken from the Day 2 reading passage**, so you may want to refer to the passage as you read to double-check your thinking. Answer the question that follows each sentence to focus on specific concepts that can only be understood if you grasp the relationships between words.

1. Based on the sentence:
"The hungry and destitute situation of the infant orphan was duly reported by the workhouse authorities to the parish authorities."
...which of these statements is **definitely** true?

   A. In the world of *Oliver Twist*, the parish supervises the workhouses.
   B. In the world of *Oliver Twist*, many poor children grow up living sad lives.
   C. In the world of *Oliver Twist*, all children live in workhouses.
   D. In the world of *Oliver Twist*, the workhouse supervises the parish.

2. Based on the lines:
"The elderly female was a woman of wisdom and experience; she knew what was good for children, and she had a very accurate perception of what was good for herself. So, she appropriated the greater part of the weekly stipend to her own use, and consigned the rising parochial generation to even a shorter allowance than was originally provided for them..."
...which of these statements is the **best description** of the "elderly female."

   A. She takes good care of all the children left with her.
   B. She takes good care of children that have money, but not poor children.
   C. She steals a great deal of money that's intended for the children.
   D. She is very wise and kind.

3. Explain the phrase:

"...a negative result usually attended the operation of her system..."

A. The elderly female often got caught misusing money.
B. The elderly female got bad reviews from her bosses at the parish.
C. The children the elderly female cared for were often sad and neglected.
D. The children the elderly female cared for often died.

fitness

Please be aware of your environment and be safe at all times. If you cannot do an exercise, just try your best.

Repeat these **exercises 4 ROUNDS**

2 - Side Bending: 15 times to each side. Note: try to touch your feet.

1 - Squats: 20 times. Note: imagine you are trying to sit on a chair.

3 - Tree Pose: Stay as long as possible. Note: do the same with the other leg.

Number Systems

1. Alicia is keeping track of the temperature in January. How would 16 degrees below freezing be represented?

    A. -16°C

    B. 16°C

    C. 32°C

    D. 0°C

2. In a card game, drawing a positive card gives you points and drawing a negative card takes away points. Which choice represents gaining 7 points?

    A. 3

    B. -4

    C. 7

    D. -7

3. A diver starts at sea level and goes down 10 feet. Which choice represents the diver's current location?

    A. 0

    B. -10

    C. 10

    D. 20

4. Draw a number line and place -4 on the number line.

5. Draw a number line and place -2 on the number line.

6. Draw a number line and place -7 on the number line.

7. What is the opposite of 6?

    A. 0

    B. 12

    C. -6

    D. $\dfrac{1}{6}$

8. What is the opposite of 22?

    A. 10

    B. -11

    C. -20

    D. -22

9. What is the opposite of 18?

    A. 9

    B. -18

    C. -9

    D. 0

10. What is the opposite of 0?

    A. 0
    B. -0
    C. -1
    D. 1

11. What is the opposite of $-\frac{1}{2}$?

    A. 2.5
    B. -2
    C. 2
    D. $\frac{1}{2}$

12. What is the opposite of -5?

    A. 0
    B. 5
    C. $-\frac{1}{5}$
    D. $\frac{1}{5}$

13. Which number is less than -54?

    A. -56
    B. 23
    C. 0
    D. -34

14. Which number is more than -23?

    A. -13
    B. -28
    C. -38
    D. -100

15. Which number is less than -7?

    A. -2
    B. -9
    C. 0
    D. 7

fitness

Please be aware of your environment and be safe at all times. If you cannot do an exercise, just try your best.

Repeat these **exercises 4 ROUNDS**

2 - Lunges: 12 times to each leg. Note: Use your body weight or books as weight to do leg lunges.

3 - Plank: 20 sec.

1 - Bend forward: 15 times. Note: try to touch your feet. Make sure to keep your back straight and if needed you can bend your knees.

4 - Abs: 20 times

Number Systems

1. What is |-5|?

  A. 3
  B. 2
  C. 5
  D. -5

2. What is |22|?

  A. -22
  B. 22
  C. 44
  D. -44

3. What is |126|?

  A. 126
  B. -126
  C. 63
  D. -63

4. What is |-278|?

  A. 100
  B. -278
  C. -178
  D. 278

5. Which number has the largest absolute value?

  A. |8|
  B. |-56|
  C. |14|
  D. |-61|

6. Which number has the largest absolute value?

  A. |-72|
  B. |82|
  C. |-32|
  D. |58|

7. Which number has the smallest absolute value?

  A. |-71|
  B. |-35|
  C. |-14|
  D. |18|

8. Which number has the smallest absolute value?

  A. |-9|
  B. |7|
  C. |-6|
  D. |-10|

9. Write < or > in the following expression:

$$|-23| \underline{\qquad} 38$$

10. Write < or > in the following expression:

$$|-45| \underline{\qquad} 43$$

11. Write < or > in the following expression:

$$|-82| \underline{\qquad} |-67|$$

12. Write < or > in the following expression:

$$17 \underline{\hspace{1cm}} |-23|$$

13. Jonathan has a balance of -$241.82. Does he have enough money to buy a TV that costs $221.90? Why or why not?

_____

_____

_____

14. Joseph is scuba diving. He is currently 10 feet below the surface. John is sailing nearby. Standing on his boat, he is currently 7 feet above sea level. Who has a higher elevation? Why?

_____

_____

15. In the scenario described in question 14, who is farther from sea level? Why?

_____

_____

fitness

Please be aware of your environment and be safe at all times. If you cannot do an exercise, just try your best.

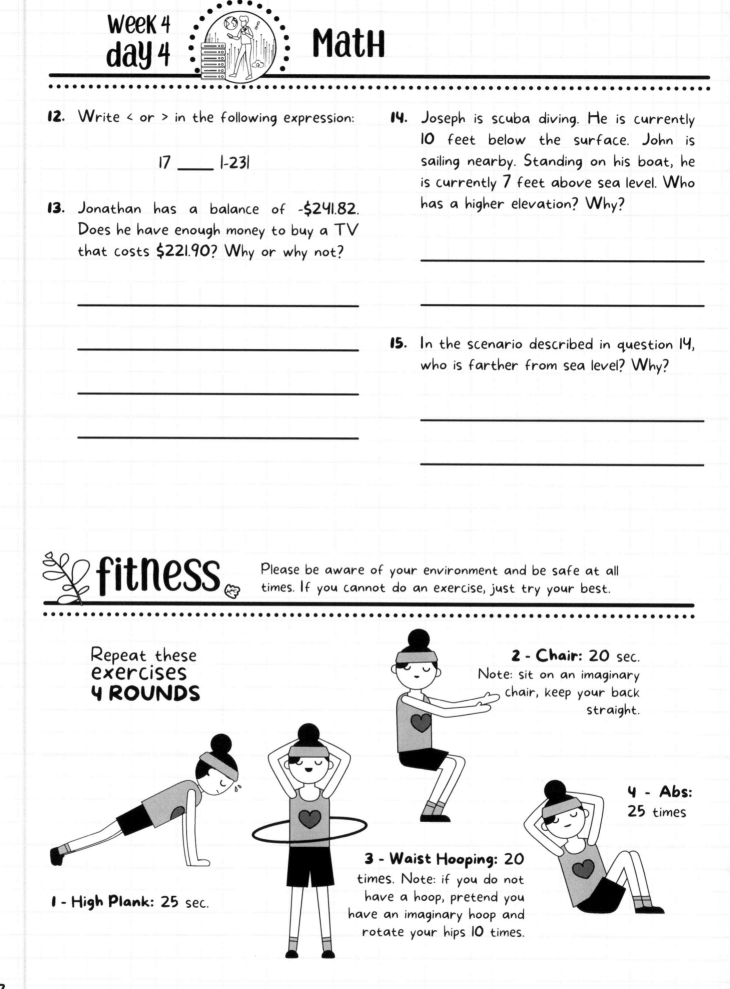

Repeat these **exercises 4 ROUNDS**

1 - **High Plank:** 25 sec.

2 - Chair: 20 sec. Note: sit on an imaginary chair, keep your back straight.

3 - Waist Hooping: 20 times. Note: if you do not have a hoop, pretend you have an imaginary hoop and rotate your hips 10 times.

4 - Abs: 25 times

MatH

Number Systems

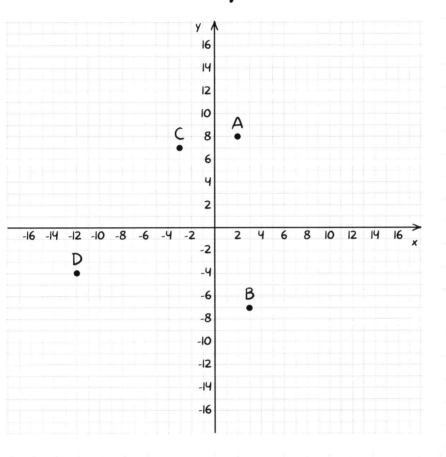

Use the coordinate plane to answer the questions below.

1. What is the location of point A?
    A. (2, -8)   C. (2, 8)
    B. (-2, 8)   D. (-2, -8)

2. What is the location of point B?
    A. (7, -3)   C. (-7, 3)
    B. (3, 7)   D. (3, -7)

3. What is the location of point C?
    A. (-3, 7)   C. (7, -3)
    B. (3, 7)   D. (-7, -3)

4. What is the location of point D?
    A. (4, 12)   C. (-12, -4)
    B. (12, 4)   D. (-4, -12)

5. Which point is located in Quadrant II?
    A.   C.
    B.   D.

6. Which point is located in Quadrant I?
    A.   C.
    B.   D.

7. Which point is located in Quadrant IV?
    A.   C.
    B.   D.

8. Which point is located in Quadrant III?

   A.   C.
   B.   D.

9. Which point could represent multiple days that received rain?

   A.   C.
   B.   D.

10. Which point could represent multiple days that represent a temperature below zero?

    A.   C.
    B.   D.

11. If a point is located at (5,0) and another point is located at (-2, 0), what is the distance between the two points?

    A. -7   C. 7
    B. 2   D. 5

12. If a point is located at (7, 5) and another point is located at (7, 15), what is the distance between the two points?

    A. 10   C. 14
    B. 12   D. 16

13. If a point is located at (0, 12) and another point is located at (0, 16), what is the distance between the two points?

    A. 1   C. 3
    B. 2   D. 4

14. If a point is located at (15, 11) and another point is located at (8, 11), what is the distance between the two points?

    A. 6   C. 8
    B. 7   D. 9

15. If a point is located at (-4, 8) and another point is located at (-4, -8), what is the distance between the two points?

    A. 4   C. 14
    B. 8   D. 16

yoga

Please be aware of your environment and be safe at all times. If you cannot do an exercise, just try your best.

3 - Chair: 30 sec.

4 - Child Pose: 30 sec.

1 - Down Dog: 30 sec.

5 - Shavasana: as long as you can. Note: think of happy moments and relax your mind.

2 - Bend Down: 30 sec.

Symbiotic Relationships

Over the last few weeks, you've looked at **populations** of plants and animals outdoors in your local environment. This week, we'll shift gears and do an inside activity that will help you think about the different kinds of relationships that populations of organisms (like plants and animals) have in the wild. When two different organisms live together in a close relationship, it's known as **symbiosis. Symbiosis** is further broken into three categories: parasitism, commensalism, and mutualism.

In a **parasitic** relationship, one organism benefits from the relationship, while the other is harmed (like how a tick can make a dog sick by feeding off of it, for example). In a **commensal** relationship, one organism benefits while the other is neither harmed nor hurt (like a barnacle on a huge whale). In a **mutualistic** relationship, both organisms benefit from the partnership (like how certain tiny birds get their food by cleaning the teeth of alligators).

Materials:

- Internet access (for research)
- 3 pieces of notepaper
- 3 pieces of plain white paper
- Art Supplies (colored pencils, markers, etc.)

experiment

Procedure:

1. Begin by taking each of your pieces of white paper and labeling the top of each one. One should say **MUTUALISM**, one should say **COMMENSALISM**, and one should say **PARASITISM**.

2. If you have questions about the three kinds of relationships described in the introduction above or feel like you need more details to understand the concepts, feel free to use the internet to help you build your own working definitions of mutualism, parasitism, and commensalism.

3. Once you are comfortable with the definition of each term, use the internet to look up at least one example of each of the three kinds of relationships. They should **not** be the one described in the above introduction. For each kind of relationship, use your notepaper to document an example and write a paragraph describing how the relationship works and why it is an example of mutualism or parasitism or commensalism.

4. On your three pieces of white paper, use your art supplies to create a picture that illustrates the relationship that you described on your notepaper. For each one, be sure to include details that help the viewer understand which organisms (plants or animals) are involved and how the relationship works.

5. After your three examples are complete, attach your notepaper to your illustration using tape, staples, or a paper clip.

6. Answer the questions below and continue to think about the three kinds of symbiotic relationships as you continue to study different organisms.

experiment

Follow-Up Questions:

1. **Brainstorm** <u>one</u> more example of a mutualistic or commensal relationship between two organisms:

   _____

   _____

   _____

2. Do you think these three types of relationships also apply to relationships between **humans**? <u>Why</u> or why not?

   _____

   _____

   _____

yoga

Please be aware of your environment and be safe at all times. If you cannot do an exercise, just try your best.

3 - Stretching: Stay as long as possible. Note: do on one leg then on another.

4 - Lower Plank: 20 sec. Note: Keep your back straight and body tight.

2 - Down Dog: 30 sec.

1 - Tree Pose: Stay as long as possible. Note: do on one leg then on another.

6 - Shavasana: 5 min. Note: this pose is very important and provides you with long term benefits. Try not to skip this. Close your eyes and imagine who you want to be and what your goals are! Always think happy thoughts.

5 - Book Pose: 20 sec. Note: Keep your core tight. Legs should be across from your eyes.

CROSSWORD

Task: Try solving this crossword puzzle! Take a look at the images and write the corresponding words in the crossword.

DOWN

ACROSS

WeeK 5

OVERVIEW OF ENGLISH CONCEPTS

Citing Evidence

Back when we talked about **writing purposeful sentences** during Week 2, we said that one of the main purposes a sentence could fulfill was "**Providing examples or evidence** that lend support for what the author is saying." This week, we'll be focusing exclusively on the concept of **evidence**. Evidence is crucial to any kind of **informational** writing as well as any analysis of **literary writing**.

It's easy to have an opinion or make a claim, but that opinion or claim has minimal value unless it's backed up with **evidence** -- words, examples, and ideas that back up your thinking, show that other smart people have approached similar ideas, and illustrate that you've actually thought about your points a great deal before writing them down. When you back up a point with evidence, you're demonstrating your skills as <u>both</u> a **reader** and a **writer**.

Finding Evidence as a Reader
When it's time for you to make a claim or articulate a viewpoint, the first step is for you to figure out **what you think or believe** based on the text and the prompt. Once you've done that, it's time to find some evidence from <u>outside yourself</u> that supports and backs up your thinking. Depending on the text you're reading and the prompt you're answering, that evidence could take the form of...
- Quotations or summaries of **key passages in the text**
  - This shows your claim is based on a strong understanding of the text
- Quotations or summaries of **quotations from other writers and critics** who have read the text as well or have explored similar ideas
  - This shows that you've done some research, while   also communicating that you're not the first person to explore these ideas (which makes you seen more **credible!**)
- Examples that connect what happened in the text **to the real world**.
  - This shows your ability to extend your thinking
- Data or statistics from a study or survey
  - This is **most useful** when you're talking about informational or nonfiction texts.

Integrating Evidence into Your Writing
Once you've found evidence, it's important to **get it into your writing**, where the reader can see (and learn from) it.
- Always explain where the evidence **came from**
  - **Who** said or wrote it? **What** book, magazine, or article was it published in? **When** did that publication come out?
- If you're using someone's **exact words** or a **direct quote** from a story as your evidence, be sure you **put that evidence inside quotation marks!**
- Be sure to include a sentence or two of your **own words** to <u>explain</u> what the evidence means to the reader and directly <u>connect</u> it to your claim or idea.

From "Oliver Twist"

By Charles Dickens

(NOTE: This passage takes place in the next chapter of *Oliver Twist*, <u>after</u> Oliver has turned 9 and been taken away from the old lady to return to the main workhouse, where he lives with a group of other boys.)

The room in which the boys were fed was a large stone hall, with a copper at one end, out of which the master, dressed in an apron for the purpose, and assisted by one or two women, ladled the gruel at meal-times; of which composition each boy had one porringer, and no more — except on festive occasions, and then he had two ounces and a quarter of bread besides. The bowls never wanted washing — the boys polished them with their spoons till they shone again; and when they had performed this operation, (which never took very long, the spoons being nearly as large as the bowls), they would sit staring at the copper with such eager eyes as if they could devour the very bricks of which it was composed; employing themselves meanwhile in sucking their fingers most assiduously, with the view of catching up any stray splashes of gruel that might have been cast thereon. Boys have generally excellent appetites. Oliver Twist and his companions suffered the tortures of slow starvation for three months; a last they got so voracious and wild with hunger, that one boy, who was tall for his age, and hadn't been used to that sort of thing, (for his father had kept a small cook's shop), hinted darkly to his companions, that unless he had another basin of gruel per diem, he was afraid he should some night eat the boy who slept next him, who happened to be a weakly youth of tender age. He had a wild, hungry eye, and they implicitly believed him. A council was held; lots were cast to see who should walk up to the master after supper that evening, and ask for more; and it fell to Oliver Twist.

The evening arrived: the boys took their places; the master in his cook's uniform stationed himself at the copper; his pauper assistants ranged themselves behind him; the gruel was served out, and a long grace was said over the short commons. The gruel disappeared, and the boys whispered each other and winked at Oliver, while his next neighbors nudged him. Child as he was, he was desperate with hunger and reckless with misery. He rose from the table, and advancing, basin and spoon in hand, to the master, said, somewhat alarmed at his own temerity —

"Please, sir, I want some more."

The master was a fat, healthy man, but he turned very pale. He gazed in stupefied astonishment on the small rebel for some seconds, and then clung for support to the copper. The assistants were paralyzed with wonder, and the boys with fear.

"What!" said the master at length, in a faint voice.

"Please, sir," replied Oliver, "I want some more."

1. According to the passage, **why** do the boys' bowls never need to be washed?

_____

_____

2. Using **your own words**, how would you describe the situation Oliver and the other boys live in?

_____

_____

_____

_____

3. Why do the boys finally decide to say something to the masters about the **portions** of food?

   A. They heard a rumor that the meals would be increasing in size.
   B. They heard a rumor that the meals would be decreasing in size.
   C. They heard that the workhouse received more money for supplies.
   D. Some of the children began talking somewhat seriously about cannibalism.

4. **How** is Oliver chosen to represent the group of boys?

   A. Oliver is the master's favorite.
   B. Oliver is the bravest.
   C. The other kids bully Oliver into doing it.
   D. The job is assigned randomly.

5. Based on what you've read so far from *Oliver Twist*, make a prediction about **what might happen next** for Oliver and his friends. How do you think the adults are going to

respond to this approach?

_____

_____

_____

_____

overview of english concepts
activities

Citing Evidence

Directions: Read each claim, argument, or point-of-view below and **review your Day 1 reading passage** to select two <u>quotations</u> or <u>important main ideas</u> that could be used as **evidence** to back up the claim being presented.

1. **CLAIM:** Oliver and the other boys are underfed.

    EVIDENCE/QUOTE #1: _____

    _____

    _____

    EVIDENCE/QUOTE #2: _____

    _____

    _____

2. **CLAIM:** The adults at the workhouse lack sympathy for the children they serve.

    EVIDENCE/QUOTE #1: _____

    _____

    _____

    EVIDENCE/QUOTE #2: _____

    _____

    _____

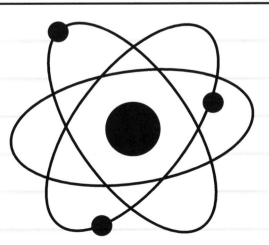

3. **CLAIM:** Oliver is brave.

   EVIDENCE/QUOTE #1: _____

   _____

   _____

   EVIDENCE/QUOTE #2: _____

   _____

   _____

fitness

Please be aware of your environment and be safe at all times. If you cannot do an exercise, just try your best.

Repeat these **exercises 4 ROUNDS**

1 - Abs: 20 times

2 - Lunges: 8 times to each leg. Note: Use your body weight or books as weight to do leg lunges.

3 - Plank: 20 sec.

4 - Run: 50m Note: Run 25 meters to one side and 25 meters back to the starting position.

From "Oliver Twist"

By Charles Dickens

(Continued from Day 1's Passage)

"Please, sir, I want some more."

The master was a fat, healthy man, but he turned very pale. He gazed in stupefied astonishment on the small rebel for some seconds, and then clung for support to the copper. The assistants were paralyzed with wonder, and the boys with fear.

"What!" said the master at length, in a faint voice.

"Please, sir," replied Oliver, "I want some more."

The master aimed a blow at Oliver's head with the ladle, pinioned him in his arms, and shrieked aloud for the supervisor.

The board were sitting in solemn conclave when Mr. Bumble rushed into the room in great excitement, and addressing the gentleman in the high chair, said —

"Mr. Limbkins, I beg your pardon, sir; — Oliver Twist has asked for more." There was a general start. Horror was depicted on every countenance.

"For more!" said Mr. Limbkins. "Compose yourself, Bumble, and answer me distinctly. Do I understand that he asked for more, after he had eaten the supper allotted by the dietary?"

"He did, sir," replied Bumble.

"That boy will be hung," said the gentleman in the white waistcoat; "I know that boy will be hung."

Nobody controverted the prophetic gentleman's opinion. An animated discussion took place. Oliver was ordered into instant confinement; and a bill was next morning pasted on the outside of the gate, offering a reward of five pounds to anybody who would take Oliver Twist off the hands of the parish. In other words, five pounds and Oliver Twist were offered to any man or woman who wanted an apprentice to any trade, business or calling.

"I never was more convinced of anything in my life," said the gentleman in the white waistcoat, as he knocked at the gate and read the bill next morning —"I never was more convinced of anything in my life, than I am that that boy will come to be hung."

As I purpose to show in the sequel whether the white-waistcoated gentleman was right or not, I should perhaps mar the interest of this narrative (supposing it to possess any at all) if I ventured to hint just yet, whether the life of Oliver Twist had this violent termination or no.

1. What is the master's **initial** reaction to Oliver asking for more food?

_____

_____

_____

2. Why do you think the board of supervisors for the workhouse wants to **remove** Oliver?

_____

_____

_____

3. What is unusual about the way the workhouse "sells" Oliver?

   A. The owners of the workhouse will get the money, not Oliver.
   B. The workhouse tries to place Oliver with someone who will teach him a trade or use him for work.
   C. The workhouse is actually offering money to anybody who will take Oliver.
   D. The board was planning on executing Oliver, but they offer to sell him at the last minute instead.

4. What is the purpose of the **final** paragraph in this passage?

   A. To engage the reader and build their interest in hearing the rest of the story
   B. To explain the complex situation that just happened in the story
   C. To make the reader connect Oliver's life to events from their own lives
   D. To provoke the reader to reflect on how far Oliver has come in his journey

5. How can aspects of this passage be seen as **comedic** or **silly**, even though the adults involved are legitimately very concerned?

_____

_____

_____

_____

_____

Citing Evidence Pt. 2

Directions: Read each claim, argument, or point-of-view below and **review your Day 2 reading passage** to select two <u>quotations</u> or <u>important main ideas</u> that could be used as **evidence** to back up the claim being presented.

1. **CLAIM:** The members of the parish board overreact to what Oliver did.

   EVIDENCE/QUOTE #1: _____

   _____

   _____

   EVIDENCE/QUOTE #2: _____

   _____

   _____

2. **CLAIM:** The members of the parish board **_really_** want to get rid of Oliver.

   EVIDENCE/QUOTE #1: _____

   _____

   _____

   EVIDENCE/QUOTE #2: _____

   _____

   _____

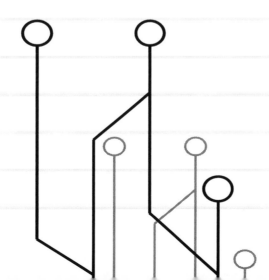

3. CLAIM: The author believes the members of the parish board are ridiculous.

EVIDENCE/QUOTE #1: _____

_____

_____

EVIDENCE/QUOTE #2: _____

_____

_____

fitness

Please be aware of your environment and be safe at all times. If you cannot do an exercise, just try your best.

Repeat these **exercises 4 ROUNDS**

2 - Side Bending: 15 times to each side. Note: try to touch your feet.

1 - Squats: 20 times. Note: imagine you are trying to sit on a chair.

3 - Tree Pose: Stay as long as possible. Note: do the same with the other leg.

Expressions and Equations

1. 3^5

    A. 15

    B. 125

    C. 243

    D. 81

2. 4^3

    A. 32

    B. 64

    C. 12

    D. 24

3. 2^4

    A. 10

    B. 12

    C. 14

    D. 16

4. 10^8

    A. 80,000,000

    B. 80,000,000

    C. 10,000,000

    D. 100,000,000

5. 1^6

    A. 1

    B. 6

    C. 7

    D. 5

6. 11^0

    A. 1

    B. 0

    C. 11

    D. 15

7. $\left(\dfrac{1}{2}\right)^4$

    A. $\dfrac{4}{16}$ C. $\dfrac{1}{4}$

    B. $\dfrac{1}{16}$ D. $\dfrac{1}{8}$

8. $\left(\dfrac{2}{3}\right)^3$

    A. $\dfrac{6}{9}$ C. $\dfrac{8}{27}$

    B. $\dfrac{4}{9}$ D. $\dfrac{8}{9}$

9. $\left(\dfrac{5}{6}\right)^2$

    A. $\dfrac{20}{25}$ C. $\dfrac{10}{12}$

    B. $\dfrac{18}{36}$ D. $\dfrac{25}{36}$

10. $\left(\dfrac{2}{7}\right)^4$

    A. $\dfrac{16}{2401}$ C. $\dfrac{8}{14}$

    B. $\dfrac{4}{28}$ D. $\dfrac{4}{49}$

11. Evaluate the expression $(x + y)^3$ when $x = 4$ and $y = 8$

    A. 1331

    B. 1728

    C. 3113

    D. 1482

12. Evaluate the expression $x^2 - y + y^2$ when $x = 4$ and $y = 8$

    A. 66
    B. 68
    C. 70
    D. 72

13. Evaluate the expression $(xy)^4$ when $x = 2$ and $y = 3$

    A. 1
    B. 1269
    C. 1296
    D. 2196

14. Evaluate the expression $(y - x)^5$ when $x = 4$ and $y = 8$

    A. 1024
    B. 1042
    C. 4012
    D. 1402

15. Evaluate the expression y^3 when $y = 5$

    A. 75
    B. 50
    C. 25
    D. 125

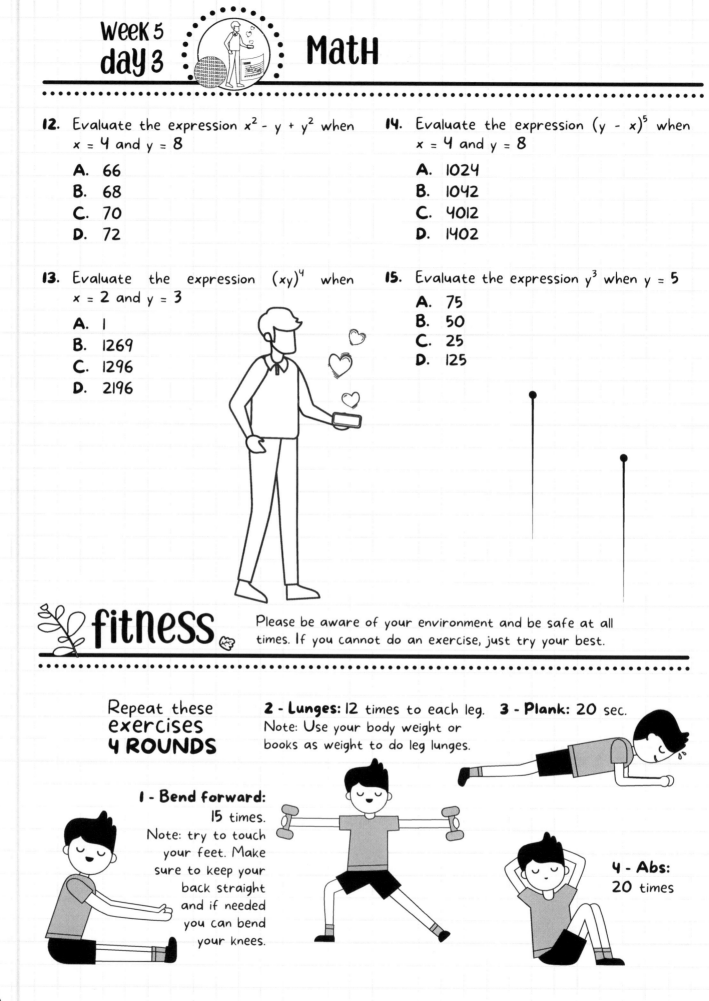

fitness

Please be aware of your environment and be safe at all times. If you cannot do an exercise, just try your best.

Repeat these **exercises 4 ROUNDS**

2 - Lunges: 12 times to each leg. Note: Use your body weight or books as weight to do leg lunges.

3 - Plank: 20 sec.

1 - Bend forward: 15 times. Note: try to touch your feet. Make sure to keep your back straight and if needed you can bend your knees.

4 - Abs: 20 times

Expressions and Equations

1. $20 - 2 \times 3^2$

   A. 1
   B. 2
   C. 3
   D. 4

2. $6 + 4 \div 2 + 3$

   A. 7
   B. 9
   C. 11
   D. 13

3. $(6^2 - 3^3) \div 2$

   A. 3.5
   B. 4
   C. 4.5
   D. 5

4. $5 \times 2^2 \div 2 + 8$

   A. 18
   B. 20
   C. 22
   D. 24

5. $52 + 8^2 - 3(4 - 2)^3$

   A. 86
   B. 88
   C. 90
   D. 92

6. What is the coefficient of the term: 35b

   A. b
   B. 35
   C. 7
   D. 5

7. What is the variable of the term: 61c

   A. c
   B. 61
   C. 6
   D. 1

8. What is the coefficient of the term: 17y

   A. y
   B. 7
   C. 17
   D. 10

9. What is the variable of the term: 89x

   A. 89
   B. 8
   C. 9
   D. x

10. Write an expression for the phrase: 10 less than m

    A. m - 10
    B. 10 - m
    C. m + 10
    D. 10 + m

11. Write an expression for the phrase: 5 more than p

    A. 5p
    B. p + 5
    C. 5(p + p)
    D. 15p

12. Write an expression for the phrase: the sum of 16 and b

    A. 16b
    B. b - 16
    C. 16 - b
    D. b + 16

13. Write an expression for the phrase: the product of 9 and w

A. $\dfrac{9}{w}$

B. $\dfrac{w}{9}$

C. $9w$

D. $w + 9$

14. Write an expression for the phrase: 16 more than the product of 11 and x

A. $11x + 16$

B. $16x + 11$

C. $27x$

D. $11 + x + 16$

15. Write an expression for the phrase: 17 less than the quotient of y and 4

A. $\dfrac{4y}{17}$

B. $\dfrac{17y}{4}$

C. $\dfrac{y}{4} - 17$

D. $\dfrac{4}{y} - 17$

fitness

Please be aware of your environment and be safe at all times. If you cannot do an exercise, just try your best.

Repeat these **exercises 4 ROUNDS**

1 - High Plank: 25 sec.

2 - Chair: 20 sec. Note: sit on an imaginary chair, keep your back straight.

3 - Waist Hooping: 20 times. Note: if you do not have a hoop, pretend you have an imaginary hoop and rotate your hips 10 times.

4 - Abs: 25 times

Expressions and Equations

Evaluate each expression with the given values.

1. $3(s - t)^2$, $s = 4$, $t = 1$
   A. 21
   B. 23
   C. 25
   D. 27

2. $2x - y^2$, $x = 7$, $y = 3.5$
   A. 2.5
   B. 1.25
   C. 1.75
   D. 2

3. $3m^2 - n$, $m = 2$, $n = 6$
   A. 3
   B. 5
   C. 6
   D. 7

4. $(2a + 2b)^2$, $a = 3$, $b = 4$
   A. 196
   B. 198
   C. 200
   D. 202

5. $2p^2 + (2q)^2$, $p = 4$, $q = 3$
   A. 66
   B. 68
   C. 70
   D. 72

6. $(4c - d + 0.2)^2$, $c = 3.1$, $d = 4.6$
   A. 58
   B. 60
   C. 62
   D. 64

7. $s + 6$, $s = 10$
   A. 16
   B. 18
   C. 20
   D. 22

8. $5 - 2t$, $t = 2$
   A. 4
   B. 2
   C. 1
   D. 5

9. $4a^4$, $a = 3$
   A. 2401
   B. 48
   C. 81
   D. 324

10. $y^2 - x^2$, $x = 10$, $y = 12$
    A. 44
    B. 46
    C. 48
    D. 50

11. $-4(n^3) + 2n$, $n = 5$
    A. -510
    B. -490
    C. -500
    D. -480

MatH

12. $9h + 2h^3$, h = 1

   A. 8
   B. 9
   C. 10
   D. 11

13. $(2a)^2b - 2c^2$, a = 2, b = 4, c = 3

   A. 46
   B. 44
   C. 48
   D. 50

14. $\dfrac{3a + c}{5b}$, a = 1, b = 3, c = 10

   A. $\dfrac{11}{13}$
   B. $\dfrac{11}{15}$
   C. $\dfrac{13}{15}$
   D. $\dfrac{12}{15}$

15. $5(b + 2)^4$, b = 0

   A. 60
   B. 70
   C. 80
   D. 90

YoGa

Please be aware of your environment and be safe at all times. If you cannot do an exercise, just try your best.

1 - Down Dog: 30 sec.

2 - Bend Down: 30 sec.

3 - Chair: 30 sec.

4 - Child Pose: 30 sec.

5 - Shavasana: as long as you can. Note: think of happy moments and relax your mind.

experiment

Primary Succession

By nature, plants want to spread and grow, but they can only live in areas that have suitable soil that will support their roots and provide access to water and nutrients. Plants and trees can't just pop up in rocky areas and expect to succeed there. Smaller organisms like mosses, lichens, and certain fungi, which are very small, simple, and do not have the complex needs of large plants, must spread into an area to prepare the soil first. This process is known as **primary succession.**

During **primary succession**, mosses, lichens, and fungi known as **pioneers** spread to a new area first to prepare the soil. Their feeding and reproductive processes soften rocky soil, making it easier for roots to grow, while also increasing access to ground water. Today, you'll do an activity that mirrors this process without needing to involve any moss or fungus!

Materials:
- Two bricks of floral foam (available at a crafting or hobby store)
- A few fresh-cut flowers
- Cool running water
- Two baking dishes (clear glass is ideal, but any will do)
- A toothpick
- Notepaper

Procedure:

1. Place one of the two floral foam bricks into one of the baking dishes (keeping it dry). This represents rocky soil <u>before</u> the process of primary succession has taken place.

2. Take the second brick of floral foam and hold it under your sink until it is wet and a little squishy (kind of like a sponge). The water represents the work that mosses, lichens, and other fungi do during primary succession. This second brick represents soil <u>that has been prepared</u> by pioneers for larger plants.

3. Place your wet piece of floral foam in the second baking dish.

4. Take your fresh cut flowers and insert a few into each piece of floral foam (you may need to poke a small hole with your toothpick first to get them in). These flowers represent different plants trying to grow in the soil represented by each brick of foam.

5. Pour about a half inch of water into the bottom of each baking dish (but not directly onto the foam).

6. Place both baking sheets near a window, where they have access to sunlight. On your notepaper, write down a few predictions about what you think might happen.

7. Wait four hours, and then check in on your flowers. Do you notice any difference between those in the wet foam (which represents prepared soil) and those in the dry foam (which represents rocky soil before the process of primary succession)? Jot down a few notes describing what you see. How much of the water is still in the bottom of each baking dish? How do the flowers look? How does the foam look?

8. Wait overnight and look at your two sets of flowers again. Again, using your notepaper, keep track of the water level in the pan, the appearance and health of the flowers, and the appearance and moisture level of the foam.

9. You can continue to make observations a few times a day for two or three days, as desired. If the water dries up in the bottom of one of the baking dishes, you can try adding some more.

10. Once one of the sets of flowers is clearly dead or dried up, clean up your materials and answer the questions below.

EXPERIMENT

Follow-Up Questions:

1. Describe the differences between what happened in the dish with the wet foam and what happened in the dish with the dry foam:

    _____

    _____

    _____

2. How did this activity help show that **ground water** has trouble reaching plants through rocky soil?

    _____

    _____

    _____

YOGA

Please be aware of your environment and be safe at all times. If you cannot do an exercise, just try your best.

3 - Stretching: Stay as long as possible. Note: do on one leg then on another.

4 - Lower Plank: 20 sec. Note: Keep your back straight and body tight.

2 - Down Dog: 30 sec.

1 - Tree Pose: Stay as long as possible. Note: do on one leg then on another.

6 - Shavasana: 5 min. Note: this pose is very important and provides you with long term benefits. Try not to skip this. Close your eyes and imagine who you want to be and what your goals are! Always think happy thoughts.

5 - Book Pose: 20 sec. Note: Keep your core tight. Legs should be across from your eyes.

MaZe

Task: The tourists are lost! Help them to find their way starting on the bottom left to find their way to the top right where the airplane will take off. Hurry - the plane leaves soon!

WeeK 6

Evaluating the Strength of Claims

Last week, we introduced the idea of using **evidence** to back up your **claims** (main points or ideas) as you write. This week, we're going to shift from the role of **writers** to that of **analytical readers and critics** to assess the strength of other people's claims. Assessing or evaluating the strength of a claim basically means reading the author's argument closely, reflecting on their evidence, and then deciding if their point makes sense and is well-argued.

When you read a text where someone is making a **claim** or **argument**, your first job as a reader is to figure out **what that claim or argument is**. Once you've identified that main point, your next job is to read the remainder of the text, assessing how well the author presents, argues, and supports that point as you go.

Strategies for Assessing Claims:

1. **Ask yourself**, "Could a reasonable person believe or agree with this claim or argument?"
   o If the answer is "No," it probably isn't a very good argument! People will write all sorts of intellectual-sounding filler and cite all sorts of "evidence" that seems vaguely connected to their main point, but if the point itself is ridiculous or doesn't seem like something a sane person would think or believe, read the rest of the text <u>very carefully and with a critical eye</u>.
2. **Break down the overarching argument** into sections, pieces, or main ideas.
   o Assessing the strength of an entire essay or book can be very difficult, but if you look at texts one section, chapter, heading, etc., at a time, it is much easier to track the development of the main claim. If you notice that one part of the argument doesn't make sense or seem correct, then that undermines the argument a great deal!
3. **Review and reflect upon the evidence** within the text.
   o Find each place the author backs themselves up with quotations, ideas from other texts or people, statistics, or graphs, and read those pieces of evidence closely. If the evidence doesn't actually agree with what the author is saying, it is not strong support!

<u>Once you've done those three things...</u>

- Write your evaluation of the claim as **<u>if you were making a claim yourself</u>**.
   o Present your **main idea** (either "This is a strong claim," or, "This is not a strong claim," etc.) in a clear concise way
   o Select **evidence of your own** to back up your thinking
     ▪ Choose quotes from the author's claim that you noticed when you were going through the three steps above and include them in your response as examples of why the claim is weak.
   o Craft an **analysis** using your own words to explain why their evidence or reasoning is off-base and show the connections (or lack of connection) between ideas.

From "Oliver Twist"

By Charles Dickens

It chanced one morning, while Oliver's affairs were in this auspicious and comfortable state, that Mr. Gamfield, chimney-sweeper, was wending his way adown the High-street, deeply cogitating in his mind his ways and means of paying certain arrears of rent, for which his landlord had become rather pressing. Mr. Gamfield's most sanguine calculation of funds could not raise them within full five pounds of the desired amount; and, in a species of arithmetical desperation, he was alternately cudgeling his brains and his donkey, when, passing the workhouse, his eyes encountered the bill on the gate.

"Wo-o!" said Mr. Gamfield to the donkey.

The donkey was in a state of profound abstraction, — wondering, probably, whether he was destined to be regaled with a cabbage-stalk or two, when he had disposed of the two sacks of soot with which the little cart was laden; so, without noticing the word of command, he jogged onwards.

Mr. Gamfield growled a fierce imprecation on the donkey generally, but more particularly on his eyes; and, running after him, bestowed a blow on his head; then, catching hold of the bridle, he gave his jaw a sharp wrench, by way of gentle reminder that he was not his own master: and, having by these means turned him round, he gave him another blow on the head, just to stun him till he came back again; and having done so, walked up to the gate to read the bill.

The gentleman with the white waistcoat was standing at the gate with his hands behind him, after having delivered himself of some profound sentiments in the board-room. Having witnessed the little dispute between Mr. Gamfield and the donkey, he smiled joyously when that person came up to read the bill, for he saw at once that Mr. Gamfield was exactly the sort of master Oliver Twist wanted. Mr. Gamfield smiled, too, as he perused the document, for five pounds was just the sum he had been wishing for; and, as to the boy with which it was encumbered, Mr. Gamfield, knowing what the dietary of the workhouse was, well knew he would be a nice small pattern, just the very thing for register stoves. So he spelt the bill through again, from beginning to end, and then, touching his fur cap in token of humility, accosted the gentleman in the white waistcoat.

"This here boy, sir, wot the parish wants to 'prentis," said Mr. Gamfield.

"Yes, my man," said the gentleman in the white waistcoat, with a condescending smile, "what of him?"

"If the parish vould like him to learn a light pleasant trade, in a good 'spectable chimbley-sweepin' bisness," said Mr. Gamfield, "I wants a 'prentis, and I'm ready to take him."

1. How would you describe **Mr. Gamfield**? How is he **similar to** or **different from** other adults we've seen in *Oliver Twist*?

_____

_____

_____

_____

2. What problem does Mr. Gamfield have with his **donkey** in the opening paragraphs of the passage?

_____

_____

3. Why is Mr. Gamfield most interested in Oliver?

A. The description of Oliver makes him sound like the perfect chimney sweep's apprentice.
B. He loves his job and wants to teach it to somebody new.
C. He wants to save him from a terrible life in the workhouse.
D. Mr. Gamfield is behind on his rent and badly needs five pounds.

4. Why does Mr. Gamfield believe Oliver will be a good chimney sweep?

A. He is skinny from being underfed.
B. He is brave and stands up for himself and others.
C. He is a hard worker and very determined.
D. He is obedient and always does what he is told.

5. How does the man in the **white waistcoat** treat Mr. Gamfield throughout the passage? What does this reveal about his character or personality?

_____

_____

_____

Evaluating the Strength of Claims (Pt. 1)

Directions: Below, you will see three **claims** or **arguments** being made about your Day 1 passage, including evidence that the person making the claim is citing. Read each claim and the evidence that backs it up, then answer the question below to assess the strength of the claim and explain why you feel that way. You **may** want to refer back to the Day 1 passage to get a full sense of the validity of the claims!

1. **CLAIM:** Mr. Gamfield is a kind man.

   EVIDENCE/QUOTE #1: "If the parish vould like him to learn a light pleasant trade, in a good 'spectable chimbley-sweepin' bisness," said Mr. Gamfield, "I wants a 'prentis, and I'm ready to take him."

   EVIDENCE/QUOTE #2: Mr. Gamfield smiled, too, as he perused the document.

   YOUR ASSESSMENT: Do you agree that Mr. Gamfield is kind? If so, explain what else made you think that way on the lines below. If you **disagree**, explain what is wrong with the evidence the person who wrote this claim has selected or discuss what they're **ignoring** or **leaving out**:

   _____

   _____

   _____

   _____

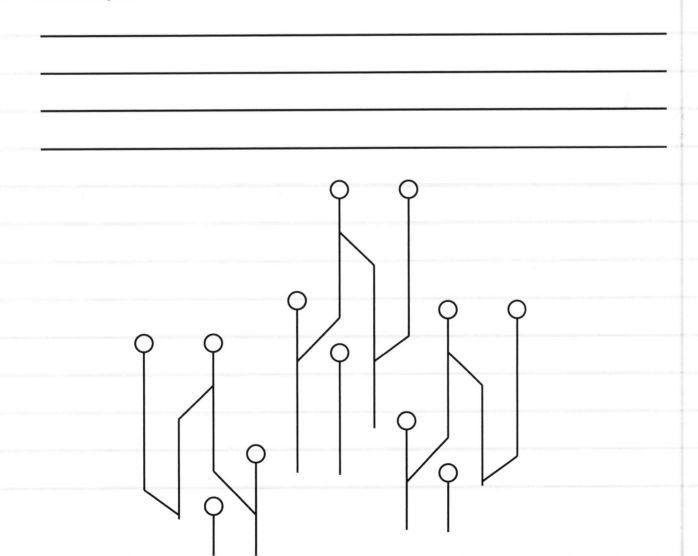

2. **CLAIM:** The gentleman in the white waistcoat badly wants Mr. Gamfield to take Oliver Twist.

EVIDENCE/QUOTE #1: "Having witnessed the little dispute between Mr. Gamfield and the donkey, he smiled joyously..."

EVIDENCE/QUOTE #2: "...he saw at once that Mr. Gamfield was exactly the sort of master Oliver Twist wanted."

YOUR ASSESSMENT: Do you agree that the gentleman in the white waistcoat definitely wants Gamfield to take Oliver? If so, explain what else made you think that way on the lines below. If you **disagree**, explain what is wrong with the evidence the person who wrote this claim has selected or discuss what they're **ignoring** or **leaving out**:

_____

_____

_____

_____

fitness

Please be aware of your environment and be safe at all times. If you cannot do an exercise, just try your best.

Repeat these **exercises 4 ROUNDS**

1 - Abs: 20 times

2 - Lunges: 8 times to each leg. Note: Use your body weight or books as weight to do leg lunges.

3 - Plank: 20 sec.

4 - Run: 50m Note: Run 25 meters to one side and 25 meters back to the starting position.

From "Oliver Twist"

By Charles Dickens

It was a large room with a great window; and behind a desk sat two old gentlemen with powdered heads, one of whom was reading the newspaper, while the other was perusing, with the aid of a pair of tortoise-shell spectacles, a small piece of parchment which lay before him. Mr. Limbkins was standing in front of the desk on one side, and Mr. Gamfield, with a partially washed face, on the other, while two or three bluff-looking men in top-boots were lounging about.

The old gentleman with the spectacles gradually dozed off over the little bit of parchment, and there was a short pause, after Oliver had been stationed by Mr. Bumble in front of the desk.

"This is the boy, your worship," said Mr. Bumble.

The old gentleman who was reading the newspaper raised his head for a moment, and pulled the other old gentleman by the sleeve, whereupon the last-mentioned old gentleman woke up.

"Oh, is this the boy?" said the old gentleman.

"This is him, sir," replied Mr. Bumble. "Bow to the magistrate, my dear."

Oliver roused himself, and made his best obeisance.

"Well," said the old gentleman, "I suppose he's fond of chimney-sweeping?"

"He dotes on it, your worship," replied Bumble, giving Oliver a sly pinch, to intimate that he had better not say he didn't.

"And he will be a sweep, will he?" inquired the old gentleman.

"If we was to bind him to any other trade to-morrow, he'd run away simultaneously, your worship," replied Bumble.

"And this man that's to be his master — you, sir — you'll treat him well, and feed him, and do all that sort of thing, — will you?" said the old gentleman.

"When I says I will, I means I will," replied Mr. Gamfield doggedly.

"You're a rough speaker, my friend, but you look an honest, open-hearted man," said the old gentleman, turning his spectacles in the direction of the candidate for Oliver's premium, whose villainous countenance was a regular stamped receipt for cruelty. But the magistrate was half blind and half childish, so he couldn't reasonably be expected to discern what other people did.

1. What is strange or inappropriate about the behavior of the **two older gentlemen** in this scene?

    _____

    _____

2. Summarize what is happening in this scene **in your own words**:

    _____

    _____

    _____

    _____

3. What major lie does Mr. Bumble tell the older gentlemen in this scene?

    A. He tells them Oliver has had a happy childhood.
    B. He tells them Oliver loves cleaning chimneys.
    C. He tells them that Oliver has never caused any trouble.
    D. He tells them that Oliver recently tried to run away.

4. What is **suggested** about the two older gentlemen (magistrates) in the final paragraph?

    A. They are corrupt.
    B. They are evil.
    C. They are heroic.
    D. They are poor judges of character.

5. How is Mr. Gamfield **different** in this passage than he was in Day 1's passage? How has the author **changed** the way you think about Gamfield by adding new details?

    _____

    _____

    _____

Evaluating the Strength of Claims (Pt. 2)

Directions: Below, you will see three **claims** or **arguments** being made about your Day 2 passage, including evidence that the person making the claim is citing. Read each claim and the evidence that backs it up, then answer the question below to assess the strength of the claim and explain why you feel that way. You **may** want to refer back to the Day 2 passage to get a full sense of the validity of the claims!

1. **CLAIM:** The two old gentlemen in this scene are bad at their jobs.

    EVIDENCE/QUOTE #1: "...one of whom was reading the newspaper, while the other was perusing, with the aid of a pair of tortoise-shell spectacles, a small piece of parchment which lay before him... The old gentleman with the spectacles gradually dozed off over the little bit of parchment"

    EVIDENCE/QUOTE #2: "'You're a rough speaker, my friend, but you look an honest, open-hearted man,' said the old gentleman, turning his spectacles in the direction of the candidate for Oliver's premium"

    YOUR ASSESSMENT: Do you agree that the two older gentlemen are bad at their jobs? If so, explain what else made you think that way on the lines below. If you **disagree**, explain what is wrong with the evidence the person who wrote this claim has selected or discuss what they're **ignoring** or **leaving out**:

    _____

    _____

    _____

    _____

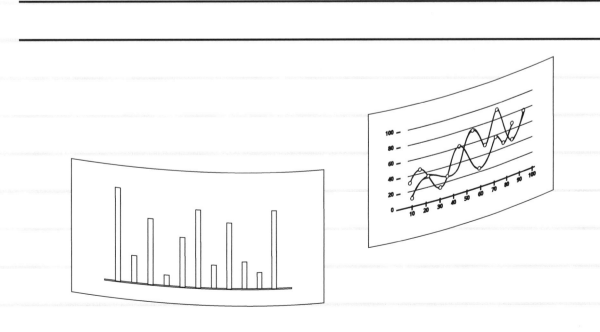

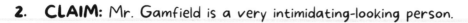
2. CLAIM: Mr. Gamfield is a very intimidating-looking person.

EVIDENCE/QUOTE #1: "Mr. Gamfield, with a partially washed face..."

EVIDENCE/QUOTE #2: "...whose villainous countenance was a regular stamped receipt for cruelty."

YOUR ASSESSMENT: Do you agree that the author describes Mr. Gamfield as being very intimidating in this scene? If so, explain what else made you think that way on the lines below. If you **disagree**, explain what is wrong with the evidence the person who wrote this claim has selected or discuss what they're **ignoring** or **leaving out**:

_____

_____

_____

_____

fitness

Please be aware of your environment and be safe at all times. If you cannot do an exercise, just try your best.

Repeat these **exercises 4 ROUNDS**

1 - Squats: 20 times. Note: imagine you are trying to sit on a chair.

2 - Side Bending: 15 times to each side. Note: try to touch your feet.

3 - Tree Pose: Stay as long as possible. Note: do the same with the other leg.

124

Expressions and Equations

1. Combine like terms to simplify the expression. $14a + 7a + 5$

   A. $21a + 5$
   B. $26a + 5$
   C. $21a$
   D. $26a$

2. Combine like terms to simplify the expression. $6d + 3d - 8b + 3b$

   A. $4d$
   B. $9d - 5b$
   C. $4b$
   D. $9d + 5b$

3. Combine like terms to simplify the expression. $12x + 7y + 9 - 6 + 3y - 10x$

   A. $13y + 2x$
   B. $12xy$
   C. $10x + 2y$
   D. $10y + 2x + 3$

4. Combine like terms to simplify the expression. $27m + 14n - 7 + 2 - 12m - 5n$

   A. $24m - 5$
   B. $15m + 9n - 5$
   C. $19n + 5$
   D. $19mn$

5. Combine like terms to simplify the expression. $16x + 42x - 2x^2 + 8x^2$

   A. $14x$
   B. $14x^2$
   C. $6x^2 + 58x$
   D. $64x$

6. Simplify by applying the distributive property. $2(x + 4)$

   A. $2x + 8$
   B. $2x + 4$
   C. $x + 8$
   D. $8x$

7. Simplify by applying the distributive property. $5(y - 2)$

   A. $-5y + 10$
   B. $15y$
   C. $-5y$
   D. $5y - 10$

8. Simplify by applying the distributive property. $10(2a + 4b - 5)$

   A. $40b + 50$
   B. $20a - 10$
   C. $20a + 40b - 50$
   D. $60a + 50$

9. Simplify by applying the distributive property. $6(3a + 9b)$

   A. $18a + 54b$
   B. $9a + 6b$
   C. $18(a + b)$
   D. $72b$

10. Simplify by applying the distributive property. $4(m - 3n)$

   A. $-8m$
   B. $4m - 12n$
   C. $16n$
   D. $12m - 4n$

MatH

11. Which expression is equivalent to 14x + 7y?

   A. 14x + 2y
   B. 7(2x + y)
   C. 7(x + 2y)
   D. 14(x + 2y)

12. Which expression is equivalent to 30a + 54b?

   A. 6(5a + 9b)
   B. 6(14a)
   C. 6(9a + 5b)
   D. 9(a + 6b)

13. Which expression is equivalent to 40m - 28n?

   A. 7(4n)
   B. 8(10m)
   C. 4(10m - 7n)
   D. 4(8m - 2n)

14. Which expression is equivalent to 21k - 18j?

   A. 21(k - 6j)
   B. 3(6j)
   C. 3(7k)
   D. 3(7k - 6j)

15. Which expression is equivalent to 45s - 35r + 10q?

   A. 5(9s)
   B. 5(9s - 7r + 2q)
   C. 5(7r)
   D. 2(5q)

fitness

Please be aware of your environment and be safe at all times. If you cannot do an exercise, just try your best.

Repeat these **exercises 4 ROUNDS**

1 - Bend forward: 15 times. Note: try to touch your feet. Make sure to keep your back straight and if needed you can bend your knees.

2 - Lunges: 12 times to each leg. Note: Use your body weight or books as weight to do leg lunges.

3 - Plank: 20 sec.

4 - Abs: 20 times

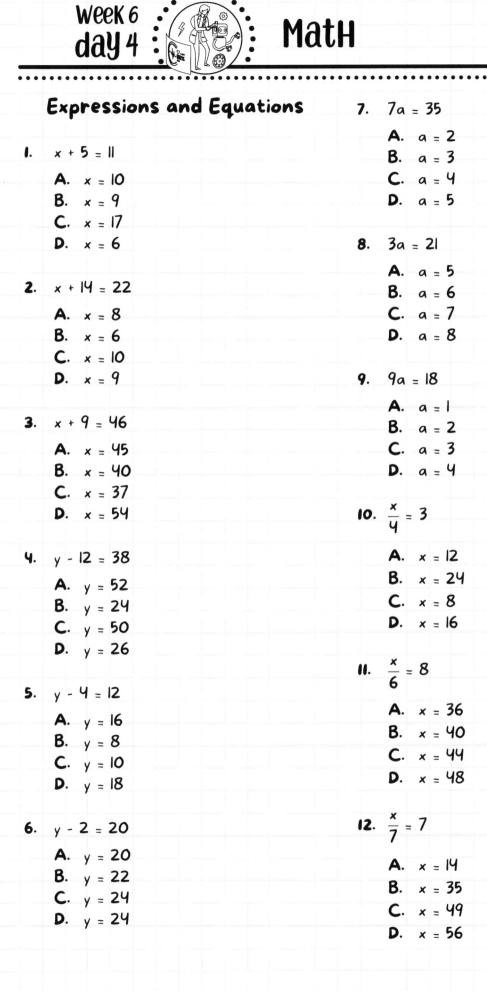

Expressions and Equations

1. $x + 5 = 11$

    A. $x = 10$
    B. $x = 9$
    C. $x = 17$
    D. $x = 6$

2. $x + 14 = 22$

    A. $x = 8$
    B. $x = 6$
    C. $x = 10$
    D. $x = 9$

3. $x + 9 = 46$

    A. $x = 45$
    B. $x = 40$
    C. $x = 37$
    D. $x = 54$

4. $y - 12 = 38$

    A. $y = 52$
    B. $y = 24$
    C. $y = 50$
    D. $y = 26$

5. $y - 4 = 12$

    A. $y = 16$
    B. $y = 8$
    C. $y = 10$
    D. $y = 18$

6. $y - 2 = 20$

    A. $y = 20$
    B. $y = 22$
    C. $y = 24$
    D. $y = 24$

7. $7a = 35$

    A. $a = 2$
    B. $a = 3$
    C. $a = 4$
    D. $a = 5$

8. $3a = 21$

    A. $a = 5$
    B. $a = 6$
    C. $a = 7$
    D. $a = 8$

9. $9a = 18$

    A. $a = 1$
    B. $a = 2$
    C. $a = 3$
    D. $a = 4$

10. $\frac{x}{4} = 3$

    A. $x = 12$
    B. $x = 24$
    C. $x = 8$
    D. $x = 16$

11. $\frac{x}{6} = 8$

    A. $x = 36$
    B. $x = 40$
    C. $x = 44$
    D. $x = 48$

12. $\frac{x}{7} = 7$

    A. $x = 14$
    B. $x = 35$
    C. $x = 49$
    D. $x = 56$

13. You are saving money to buy a new video game system. The cost of the video game is $245. You are trying to figure out how many weeks it will take you to save the game. What is the dependent variable in this situation?

_____

_____

14. You are saving money to buy a new video game system. The cost of the video game is $245. You are trying to figure out how many weeks it will take you to save the game. What is the independent variable in this situation?

_____

_____

15. You are saving money to buy a new video game system. The cost of the video game is $245. You are trying to figure out how many weeks it will take you to save the game. You earn $15 a week doing chores. Write an equation to represent the situation.

_____

_____

_____

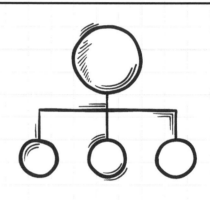

fitness

Please be aware of your environment and be safe at all times. If you cannot do an exercise, just try your best.

Repeat these **exercises 4 ROUNDS**

2 - Chair: 20 sec. Note: sit on an imaginary chair, keep your back straight.

1 - High Plank: 25 sec.

3 - Waist Hooping: 20 times. Note: if you do not have a hoop, pretend you have an imaginary hoop and rotate your hips 10 times.

4 - Abs: 25 times

128

Expressions and Equations

1. What does this graph represent?

(number line with open circle at 3)

-5 -4 -3 -2 -1 0 1 2 3 4 5

A. $x < -3$ C. $x > 3$

B. $x < 3$ D. $x > -3$

2. What does this graph represent?

(number line with open circle at -2)

-5 -4 -3 -2 -1 0 1 2 3 4 5

A. $x < -2$ C. $x > -2$

B. $x < 2$ D. $x > 2$

3. What does this graph represent?

(number line with open circle at 1)

-5 -4 -3 -2 -1 0 1 2 3 4 5

A. $x < -1$ C. $x > 1$

B. $x < 1$ D. $x > -1$

4. What does this graph represent?

(number line with open circle at -4)

-5 -4 -3 -2 -1 0 1 2 3 4 5

A. $x < 4$ C. $x > -4$

B. $x < -4$ D. $x > 4$

5. What does this graph represent?

(number line with open circle at 5)

-5 -4 -3 -2 -1 0 1 2 3 4 5

A. $x < -5$ C. $x > -5$

B. $x < -5$ D. $x > 5$

6. What does this graph represent?

(number line with open circle at -5)

-5 -4 -3 -2 -1 0 1 2 3 4 5

A. $x < -5$ C. $x > -5$

B. $x < 5$ D. $x > -5$

7. Which x value satisfies the following inequality: $x + 3 > 10$

A. $x = 7$

B. $x = 8$

C. $x = 6$

D. $x = 4$

8. Which x value satisfies the following inequality: $x + 5 < 4$

A. $x = 2$

B. $x = -2$

C. $x = -1$

D. $x = 1$

9. Which x value satisfies the following inequality: $x - 8 < 9$

A. $x = 18$

B. $x = 20$

C. $x = 16$

D. $x = 17$

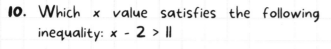

10. Which *x* value satisfies the following inequality: *x* - 2 > 11

    A. *x* = 14

    B. *x* = 13

    C. *x* = 12

    D. *x* = 11

11. Which *x* value satisfies the following inequality: 4*x* > 16

    A. *x* = 2

    B. *x* = 3

    C. *x* = 4

    D. *x* = 5

12. Which *x* value satisfies the following inequality: 8*x* < 56

    A. *x* = 7

    B. *x* = 6

    C. *x* = 8

    D. *x* = 10

13. Water freezes at 32°F. Which inequality represents the temperatures of frozen water?

    A. *x* > 0

    B. *x* < 0

    C. *x* < 32

    D. *x* > 32

14. Our car cost $24,000 not including taxes. Which inequality represents how much money we needed to save to buy the car?

    A. *x* > 24000

    B. *x* < 24000

    C. *x* < 6000

    D. *x* > 6000

15. Certain sea creatures live deeper than 32 meters under sea level. Which inequality represents where the deep sea creatures live?

    A. *x* < -32

    B. *x* > -32

    C. *x* > 32

    D. *x* < 32

yoga

Please be aware of your environment and be safe at all times. If you cannot do an exercise, just try your best.

1 - **Down Dog:** 30 sec.

2 - **Bend Down:** 30 sec.

3 - **Chair:** 30 sec.

4 - **Child Pose:** 30 sec.

5 - **Shavasana:** as long as you can. Note: think of happy moments and relax your mind.

experiment

Building an Ecosystem

Over the last five weeks, we've looked a lot at plants and animals within ecosystems. We've studied biodiversity and populations and started to think about how plants and animals spread to new areas. Today, we'll put a lot of that thinking together by **creating an ecosystem in a bottle!**

Your ecosystem will have **two** living elements: a plant and an animal (technically a fish) that will work together to survive and thrive. This activity involves a lot of fun crafting on day one, but also creates something that you can hang onto for weeks or months to come!

Materials:

- An empty, clean, dry **2**-liter bottle
- A pair of scissors or a crafting knife (be <u>extremely</u> careful with these!)
- An adult
- Cotton string (about **2** feet)
- Three paper coffee filters
- Cool running water
- One or two small goldfish (available at the pet store)
- Fish food flakes (available at the pet store)
- A little gravel or some aquarium rocks (cleaned and rinsed)
- A small plant from a garden center (kitchen herbs work great)

Procedure:

1. Using scissors or a craft knife, **have an adult cut** the top off your 2-liter bottle below the dome at the top and around where the sides straighten out. Try to keep the edge as clean as possible. Be careful of sharp edges when you're done!

2. Place your gravel or aquarium rocks in the <u>bottom</u> of the bottle. Then, fill the bottom of the bottle between a third and halfway with cool (not cold or warm) water.

3. Place your goldfish in the water.

4. Using scissors or a craft knife, **have an adult** cut a small hole above the water line that you can use to drop a few flakes of fish food down to the fish each day.

5. Set the bottom of the bottle (which is now a mini aquarium) aside and grab the top, turning it upside down so you're looking at the side with the large opening (like a funnel)

6. Put your paper coffee filters down inside the wide side of the "funnel" you're holding.

7. Using your scissors, poke a small hole in the very center of your coffee filters.

8. Tie a knot in the end of your cotton string and feed it down through the filters so it touches the water below. The knot should prevent the string from falling through.

9. Transfer your small plant from its plastic container to the coffee filters, pushing downward gently on the soil to keep it in place. You may need to add a small amount of additional soil so that it sits nicely in the filters.

10. Place the funnel you've just created on top of the bottom part of the bottle, with the plant facing up. You've now created a self-contained ecosystem: nutrients and water from below will climb up the string to feed the plant, and the water you feed the plant will drip down through the filters and toward the fish.

11. Answer the questions below, clean up your materials, and then place your new ecosystem in a sunny place to see how long it will continue to thrive!

experiment

Follow-Up Questions:

1. How does this ecosystem display a **mutualistic** relationship?

_____

_____

_____

2. How does this activity connect to the **primary succession** activity from last week?

_____

_____

_____

 yoga

Please be aware of your environment and be safe at all times. If you cannot do an exercise, just try your best.

3 - Stretching: Stay as long as possible.
Note: do on one leg then on another.

4 - Lower Plank: 20 sec.
Note: Keep your back straight and body tight.

2 - Down Dog: 30 sec.

6 - Shavasana: 5 min.
Note: this pose is very important and provides you with long term benefits. Try not to skip this. Close your eyes and imagine who you want to be and what your goals are! Always think happy thoughts.

5 - Book Pose: 20 sec.
Note: Keep your core tight. Legs should be across from your eyes.

1 - Tree Pose: Stay as long as possible. Note: do on one leg then on another.

Task: Help Max find his way to the bees through the maze.

WEEK 7

OVERVIEW Of ENGLISH CONCEPTS

Connotative vs. Denotative Meaning

Over the first half of the summer, we've looked closely at sentences and paragraphs to focus on communicating information, ideas, and messages in a clear, purposeful, reader-friendly way. This week, we're going to zoom in even further and think about **individual words** and their definitions.

As you've noticed by now, many words have several different definitions. For example, a "can" can be something metal that food is stored in, or "can" can also be used as a word that means "I am able to do something". However, some words contain **feelings** that go beyond their dictionary definition. Those emotions and associations that go with a word are known as its **connotative meaning**.

Key Terms
Denotative Meaning: The dictionary definition of a word
Connotative Meaning: The feelings, emotions, and associations that go with a certain word

Let's Look at Some Examples:
- Sally can be very **picky** about her food.
- Sally can be very **selective** about her food.
- Sally can be very **meticulous** about her food.

All three of these sentences **communicate the same general idea** because picky, selective, and meticulous all have very close **denotative** (dictionary) definitions. However, each word carries different **connotations**.
- **PICKY** has a **negative** connotation, because when someone is "picky," it often causes an inconvenience for other people. When you describe someone as "picky," you're saying their intense selectiveness borders on the annoying or inconvenient.
- **SELECTIVE** has a **neutral** connotation because it simply communicates that someone is particular about the selections that they make. The word does not carry any strong connotations one way or the other.
- **METICULOUS** has a **positive** connotation, because when someone is said to be "meticulous," they are usually a very smart, analytical person.

So, as you can see, **connotations** are important to consider, both as a reader and a writer.
- When you **read**, be sure you think about each word in a sentence, especially sentences that seem **important!**
- When you **write** (especially if you're working on a second or third draft), use words with strong connotations, as they provide variety to your vocabulary and provide you with another pathway to communicate meaning beyond explicitly stating things.

From "Sense and Sensibility"

By Jane Austen

The family of Dashwood had long been settled in Sussex. Their estate was large, and their residence was at Norland Park, in the center of their property, where, for many generations, they had lived in so respectable a manner as to engage the general good opinion of their surrounding acquaintance. The recent owner of this estate was a single man, who lived to a very advanced age, and who for many years of his life, had a constant companion and housekeeper in his sister. But her death, which happened ten years before his own, produced a great alteration in his home; for to supply her loss, he invited and received into his house the family of his nephew Mr. Henry Dashwood, the legal inheritor of the Norland estate, and the person to whom he intended to bequeath it. In the society of his nephew and niece, and their children, the old Gentleman's days were comfortably spent. His attachment to them all increased. The constant attention of Mr. and Mrs. Henry Dashwood to his wishes, which proceeded not merely from interest, but from goodness of heart, gave him every degree of solid comfort which his age could receive; and the cheerfulness of the children added a relish to his existence.

By a former marriage, Mr. Henry Dashwood had one son: by his present lady, three daughters. The son, a steady respectable young man, was amply provided for by the fortune of his mother, which had been large, and half of which transferred to him on his coming of age. By his own marriage, likewise, which happened soon afterwards, he added to his wealth. To him therefore the succession to the Norland estate was not so really important as to his sisters; for their fortune, independent of what might arise to them from their father's inheriting that property, could be but small. Their mother had nothing, and their father only seven thousand pounds in his own disposal; for the remaining portion of his first wife's fortune was also secured to her child, and he had only a life-interest in it.

1. How did the Dashwood family come to live with the Old Gentleman?

_____

_____

2. How was Mr. Dashwood's **first** wife different from his **second** wife?

_____

_____

_____

_____

3. According to the text, how many **children** does Mr. Henry Dashwood have?

   A. 2
   B. 3
   C. 4
   D. 5

4. Does the description of the Old Gentleman as "a single man, who lived to a **very advanced age**" carry <u>positive</u> or <u>negative</u> connotations?

   A. Positive, because saying someone lived to "an advanced age" seems like a compliment or accomplishment.
   B. Negative, because they are calling him old.
   C. Positive, because the word "very" shows that something is good.
   D. Negative, because they say he was "single," which shows that nobody loved him.

5. Based on Paragraph 2, how are the Dashwoods in a complex **financial** situation?

   _____

   _____

   _____

   _____

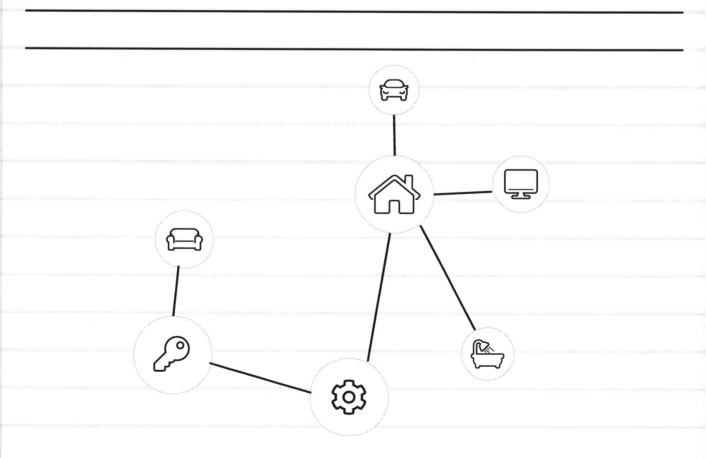

Identifying Words with Connotative Meanings

Directions: Each sentence below contains a word or phrase that carries a positive or negative connotative meaning. Read each sentence carefully and <u>**underline**</u> words that have strong connotations. On the lines below each sentence, explain whether the word has a **positive** or **negative** connotation, then **brainstorm** a <u>synonym</u> for the word you underlined that has the **opposite** connotation (so, if the word is **negative**, brainstorm a **positive** synonym).

1. Mike can be very lazy with the way he manages his time.

    - POSITIVE or NEGATIVE? _____

    - What's a **synonym** with the **opposite** connotation? _____

2. The courageous knight decided to fight the dragon, even though it had eaten every other knight who had tested it.

    - POSITIVE or NEGATIVE? _____

    - What's a **synonym** with the **opposite** connotation? _____

3. My dad's new apartment is tiny.

    - POSITIVE or NEGATIVE? _____

    - What's a **synonym** with the **opposite** connotation? _____

4. Our dog can be very energetic when she's trying to get your attention.

    - POSITIVE or NEGATIVE? _____

    - What's a **synonym** with the **opposite** connotation? _____

5. Getting your driver's license can be a tedious process.

    - POSITIVE or NEGATIVE? _____

    - What's a **synonym** with the **opposite** connotation? _____

fitness

Please be aware of your environment and be safe at all times. If you cannot do an exercise, just try your best.

Repeat these **exercises 4 ROUNDS**

1 - Abs: 20 times

2 - Lunges: 8 times to each leg. Note: Use your body weight or books as weight to do leg lunges.

3 - Plank: 20 sec.

4 - Run: 50m Note: Run 25 meters to one side and 25 meters back to the starting position.

From "Sense and Sensibility"

By Jane Austen

(Continued from Day 1's Passage)

The old gentleman died: his will was read, and like almost every other will, gave as much disappointment as pleasure. He was neither so unjust, nor so ungrateful, as to keep his estate from his nephew; — but he left it to him on such terms as destroyed half the value of the bequest. Mr. Dashwood had wished for it more for the sake of his wife and daughters than for himself or his son; — but to his son, and his son's son, a child of four years old, it was secured, in such a way, as to leave to himself no power of providing for those who were most dear to him, and who most needed a provision by any charge on the estate, or by any sale of its valuable woods. The whole was tied up for the benefit of this child, who, in occasional visits with his father and mother at Norland, had so far gained on the affections of his uncle, by such attractions as are by no means unusual in children of two or three years old; an imperfect articulation, an earnest desire of having his own way, many cunning tricks, and a great deal of noise, as to outweigh all the value of all the attention which, for years, he had received from his niece and her daughters. He meant not to be unkind, however, and, as a mark of his affection for the three girls, he left them a thousand pounds a-piece.

Mr. Dashwood's disappointment was, at first, severe; but his temper was cheerful and sanguine; and he might reasonably hope to live many years, and by living economically, lay by a considerable sum from the produce of an estate already large, and capable of almost immediate improvement. But the fortune, which had been so late in coming, was his only one year. He survived his uncle no longer; and ten thousand pounds, including the late legacies, was all that remained for his widow and daughters.

His son was sent for as soon as his danger was known, and to him Mr. Dashwood recommended, with all the strength and urgency which illness could command, the interest of his mother-in-law and sisters.

1. Which aspects of the Old Gentleman's will seem fair or valuable to the Dashwood family?

   _____

   _____

2. Which aspects of the Old Gentleman's will seem unfair or potentially destructive for the Dashwood family?

   _____

   _____

3. Which of these people benefits the most from the Old Gentleman's will?

   A. The Old Gentleman
   B. Mr. Dashwood
   C. Mr. Dashwood's son
   D. Mr. Dashwood's daughters

4. What happens to Mr. Dashwood about a year after the Old Gentleman dies?

   A. He falls ill.
   B. He inherits more money.
   C. His daughters all move out and leave him alone in the manor.
   D. He learns his son is dead.

5. If **you** were in Mr. Dashwood's position, what would you say to your son to try and convince him to help your daughters?

   _____

   _____

   _____

   _____

OVERVIEW OF ENGLISH CONCEPTS
ACTIVITIES

Creating Connotative Meaning

Directions: Each sentence below contains an underlined word that has a fairly neutral, **denotative** meaning. Your job is to read the sentence and choose a stronger, better word with a **connotation** that can replace the underlined word. Once you've chosen your replacement word, explain the **connotative** meaning of the new sentence on the lines below.

1. Stephania <u>walked</u> to the store to buy a loaf of bread.

    - **REPLACEMENT WORD:** _____

    - Explain the **Connotation:** _____

    _____

    _____

2. Marjorie was <u>surprised</u> to see her husband return home early from his deployment.

    - **REPLACEMENT WORD:** _____

    - Explain the **Connotation:** _____

    _____

    _____

3. My sister Caroline is always very <u>interested</u> when it comes to other people's business.

- **REPLACEMENT WORD:** _____

- Explain the **Connotation:** _____

_____

_____

4. Breakfast cereals are easy to eat on the go, but they are usually <u>bad for you</u>.

- **REPLACEMENT WORD:** _____

- Explain the **Connotation:** _____

_____

_____

fitness

Please be aware of your environment and be safe at all times. If you cannot do an exercise, just try your best.

Repeat these
exercises
4 ROUNDS

2 - Side Bending:
15 times to each
side. Note: try to
touch your feet.

1 - Squats:
20 times.
Note: imagine you
are trying to sit
on a chair.

3 - Tree Pose:
Stay as long
as possible.
Note: do the same
with the other leg.

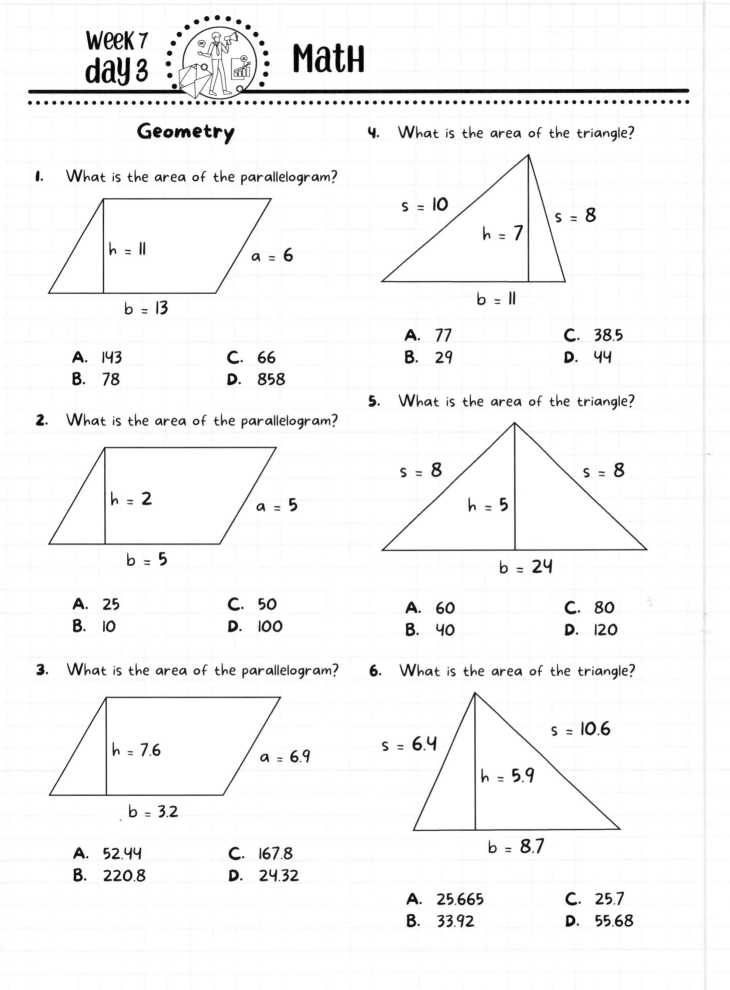

Geometry

1. What is the area of the parallelogram?

h = 11
a = 6
b = 13

A. 143   C. 66
B. 78   D. 858

2. What is the area of the parallelogram?

h = 2
a = 5
b = 5

A. 25   C. 50
B. 10   D. 100

3. What is the area of the parallelogram?

h = 7.6
a = 6.9
b = 3.2

A. 52.44   C. 167.8
B. 220.8   D. 24.32

4. What is the area of the triangle?

s = 10
h = 7
s = 8
b = 11

A. 77   C. 38.5
B. 29   D. 44

5. What is the area of the triangle?

s = 8
s = 8
h = 5
b = 24

A. 60   C. 80
B. 40   D. 120

6. What is the area of the triangle?

s = 10.6
s = 6.4
h = 5.9
b = 8.7

A. 25.665   C. 25.7
B. 33.92   D. 55.68

Geometry

7. What is the area of the triangle? $b = \dfrac{5}{7}$, $h = \dfrac{2}{3}$, $s = \dfrac{1}{6}, \dfrac{2}{3}$

   A. $\dfrac{5}{84}$ B. $\dfrac{5}{21}$ C. $\dfrac{1}{18}$ D. $\dfrac{1}{27}$

8. What is the area of the triangle? $b = 4\dfrac{4}{6}$, $h = 3\dfrac{3}{7}$, $s = 2\dfrac{1}{6}, 5\dfrac{5}{9}$

   A. 2   C. 8
   B. 4   D. 16

9. What is the area of the triangle? $b = 1\dfrac{4}{9}$, $h = 4\dfrac{6}{10}$, $s = 6\dfrac{2}{8}, 10\dfrac{3}{4}$

   A. 1.8   C. 2.7
   B. 2.2   D. 3.3

10. What is the area of the trapezoid?

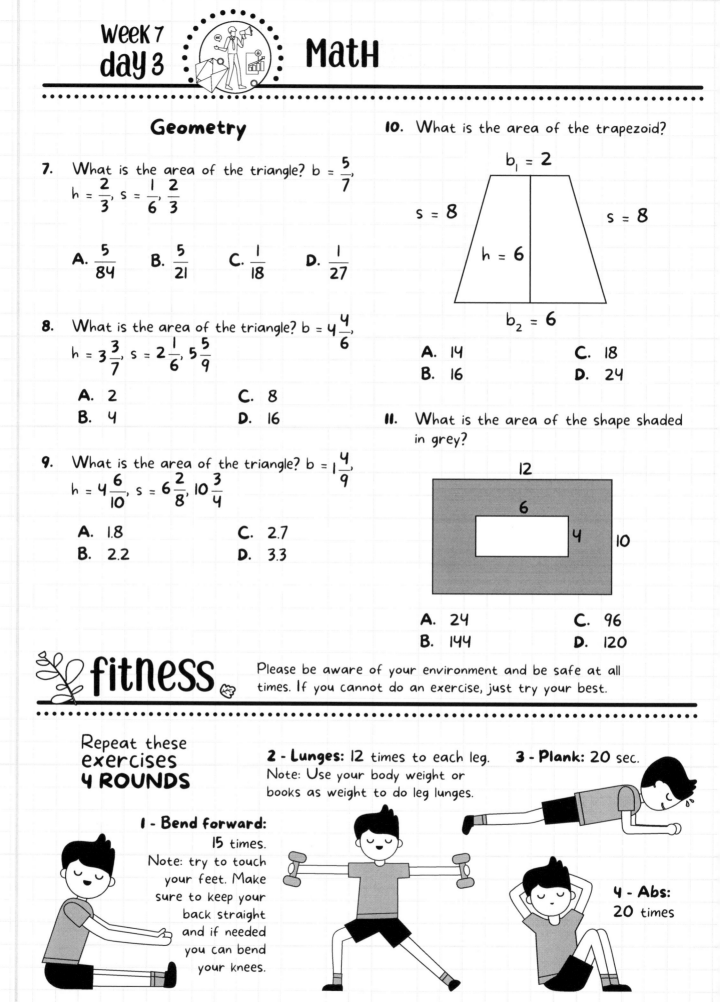

$b_1 = 2$

$s = 8$ $s = 8$

$h = 6$

$b_2 = 6$

   A. 14   C. 18
   B. 16   D. 24

11. What is the area of the shape shaded in grey?

12

6

4

10

   A. 24   C. 96
   B. 144   D. 120

fitness

Please be aware of your environment and be safe at all times. If you cannot do an exercise, just try your best.

Repeat these **exercises 4 ROUNDS**

2 - Lunges: 12 times to each leg. Note: Use your body weight or books as weight to do leg lunges.

3 - Plank: 20 sec.

1 - Bend forward: 15 times. Note: try to touch your feet. Make sure to keep your back straight and if needed you can bend your knees.

4 - Abs: 20 times

Volume

1. What is the volume of the rectangular prism?

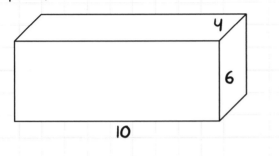

4

6

10

A. 60   C. 220
B. 200   D. 240

2. What is the volume of the rectangular prism?

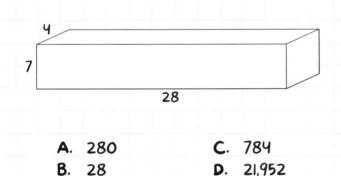

4

7

28

A. 280   C. 784
B. 28   D. 21,952

3. What is the volume of the rectangular prism?

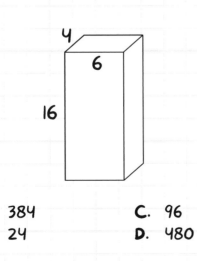

4

6

16

A. 384   C. 96
B. 24   D. 480

4. What is the volume of the rectangular prism?

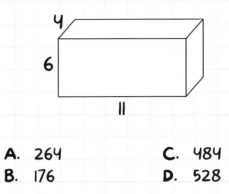

4

6

11

A. 264   C. 484
B. 176   D. 528

5. What is the volume of the rectangular prism?

2

3

15

A. 80   C. 100
B. 90   D. 110

6. What is the volume of a cube with a side of 0.8?

A. 6.4   C. 0.64
B. 5.12   D. 0.512

7. What is the volume of a cube with a side of 23?

A. 484   C. 12,167
B. 529   D. 10,648

8. What is the volume of a cube with a side of $\frac{3}{4}$?

A. 0.75   C. 0.56
B. 0.42   D. 0.23

9. What is the volume of a cube with a side of 2.4?

   A. 7.2   C. 9.6
   B. 13.824   D. 33.17

10. What is the volume of a cube with a side of $5\frac{1}{3}$?

   A. $\frac{6}{2}$ C. $\frac{4096}{27}$
   B. $\frac{256}{9}$ D. $\frac{125}{9}$

11. What is the volume of the rectangular prism?

   [diagram: rectangular prism with dimensions $\frac{3}{4}$, $4\frac{2}{3}$, $1\frac{1}{2}$]

   A. 4.5   C. 5
   B. 4.75   D. 5.25

12. What is the volume of the rectangular prism?

   [diagram: rectangular prism with dimensions $4\frac{1}{2}$, $\frac{1}{8}$, $8\frac{2}{3}$]

   A. $4\frac{7}{8}$ B. $5\frac{41}{84}$ C. $2\frac{27}{44}$ D. $3\frac{4}{7}$

13. A prism has a volume of 126. Its width is 3 and its height is 7. What is its length?

   A. 5   B. 6   C. 7   D. 8

14. A prism has a volume of 198. Its length is 2 and its height is 11. What is its width?

   A. 11   B. 10   C. 9   D. 8

15. A prism has a volume of 8064. Its width is 16 and its length is 24. What is its height?

   A. 18   B. 19   C. 20   D. 21

fitness

Please be aware of your environment and be safe at all times. If you cannot do an exercise, just try your best.

Repeat these exercises 4 ROUNDS

1 - High Plank: 25 sec.

3 - Waist Hooping: 20 times. Note: if you do not have a hoop, pretend you have an imaginary hoop and rotate your hips 10 times.

2 - Chair: 20 sec. Note: sit on an imaginary chair, keep your back straight.

4 - Abs: 25 times

Geometry

1. The parallelogram has an area of 96. Its height is 8. What is the base?

   A. 6   C. 10
   B. 8   D. 12

2. The parallelogram has an area of 6. Its height is 1.5. What is the base?

   A. 3   C. 4
   B. 6   D. 5

3. The parallelogram has an area of 99. Its base is 9. What is the height?

   A. 10   C. 12
   B. 11   D. 13

4. The parallelogram has an area of 884. Its base is 26. What is the height?

   A. 32   C. 36
   B. 34   D. 38

5. The triangle has an area of 144. Its height is 16. What is the base?

   A. 18   C. 22
   B. 20   D. 24

6. The triangle has an area of 4. Its height is 2. What is the base?

   A. 1   C. 4
   B. 2   D. 8

7. The triangle has an area of 60. Its base is 10. What is the height?

   A. 6   C. 10
   B. 8   D. 12

8. The triangle has an area of 120. Its base is 15. What is the height?

   A. 14   C. 18
   B. 16   D. 20

9. A wall measures 12 feet by 8 feet. In its center is a door that measures 3 feet by 7 feet. If I want to paint the wall but not the door, how much area in square feet should I expect to cover?

   A. 75   C. 85
   B. 80   D. 90

10. A garden measures 10 meters by 11 meters. It contains a rectangular fountain measuring 4 meters by 7 meters. If I want to cover the garden with sod, how much area in square meters should I expect to cover?

    A. 78   C. 82
    B. 80   D. 84

11. Our kitchen measures 18 feet by 14 feet. In its center is an island that measures 3 feet by 5 feet. If we want to install a new floor, how much area should we expect to cover?

    A. 267   C. 232
    B. 252   D. 237

149

12. After we install the new floor, we are going to add new tiles to our kitchen counters. Each tile covers 1 ft². If our counter is pictured below, how many tiles will we need?

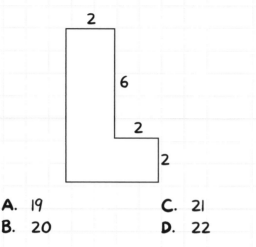

2

6

2

2

A. 19   C. 21
B. 20   D. 22

13. The elementary school playground is 15 meters by 12 meters. It is surrounded by a creek that is 2 meters wide all around the playground. If the playground and creek are going to be surrounded by a fence, what is the area the fence will surround?

A. 130   C. 304
B. 180   D. 360

14. Nathaniel is planting a triangular flowerbed in his front yard. He buys mulch to cover the flowerbed. Each bag of mulch covers 12 square feet. If the base of the flowerbed is 16 feet and the height is 6 feet, how many bags of mulch will Nathaniel need?

A. 5   C. 3
B. 2   D. 4

15. Amelia is planning a triangular fountain for her rectangular garden. The base is 8 meters and the height is 4 meters. If her garden is 16 meters by 11 meters, how much space in square meters will be covered by the fountain?

A. 16   C. 160
B. 32   D. 176

yoga

Please be aware of your environment and be safe at all times. If you cannot do an exercise, just try your best.

3 - **Chair:** 30 sec.

4 - **Child Pose:** 30 sec.

1 - **Down Dog:** 30 sec.

5 - **Shavasana:** as long as you can. Note: think of happy moments and relax your mind.

2 - **Bend Down:** 30 sec.

experiment

Natural Selection

Over the last six weeks, you've carried out several investigations focusing on how **organisms** like plants and animals survive and thrive in their **ecosystems**. This week, we'll start to think about how **populations** are maintained and refined over time through a process known as **natural selection.**

Natural selection is the process that ensures that animals and plants that are able to live successfully with good traits and adaptations for their ecosystem are able to reproduce and pass their genetics on. Other organisms that lack desirable traits or adaptations for survival, food acquisition, and mate attraction die without reproducing as often due to the process of **natural selection.**

Today, you'll be doing an activity with a group of friends or family members to help you understand the concept of natural selection just a little better!

Materials:

- At least two other people (friends or family members are perfect)
- 1 piece of red construction paper
- 1 piece of green construction paper
- 1 piece of brown construction paper
- 1 piece of blue construction paper
- 1 piece of black construction paper
- 3 different kinds of small, round candies (ideally, representing a variety of colors and at least a slight variety in size)
- 1 large bowl
- Notepaper

Procedure:

1. Open the different candies and sort them based on **type of candy** and **color**. On your notepaper, write down **how many candies of each color** are in your combined batch.

2. Once you've counted out the different candies, mix them together in the bowl and bring that bowl, your notepaper, and the construction paper to a table or other flat, clean surface where you and your friends or family members can sit.

3. Take the red piece of construction paper and place it in the center of the table. Dump about 1/5 of the candies out onto the paper and carefully spread them into an even layer.

4. Then, have everybody seated at the table close their eyes and count to ten out loud. After counting to ten, everybody should open their eyes and grab the first 3 candies they notice.

5. Once everybody has grabbed 3 candies, take out your notepaper and write down which candies were grabbed from the red paper. After you've done that, everybody can set the candy they grabbed aside to eat later.

6. Return the candies that nobody grabbed to the large bowl.

7. Repeat Steps **3-6** for the green paper.

8. Repeat Steps **3-6** for the brown paper

9. Repeat Steps **3-6** for the blue paper

10. Repeat Steps **3-6** for the black paper

11. Once you've carried out this experiment for all five colors of paper, review your notes as a group and think about each colored paper as being a different "ecosystem." Discuss which candies were the best adapted for "survival" in each ecosystem. What common themes did you notice? Which candies did you grab the most and least of? Why do you think that was?

12. Once your group discussion is complete, answer the questions below and clean up your materials.

Follow-Up Questions:

1. Which candies seemed to be the best at "surviving" throughout the experiment? Why do you think people didn't grab them?

_____

_____

_____

2. How was this activity connected to the idea of camouflage?

_____

_____

_____

yoga

Please be aware of your environment and be safe at all times. If you cannot do an exercise, just try your best.

3 - Stretching: Stay as long as possible. Note: do on one leg then on another.

4 - Lower Plank: 20 sec. Note: Keep your back straight and body tight.

2 - Down Dog: 30 sec.

6 - Shavasana: 5 min. Note: this pose is very important and provides you with long term benefits. Try not to skip this. Close your eyes and imagine who you want to be and what your goals are! Always think happy thoughts.

5 - Book Pose: 20 sec. Note: Keep your core tight. Legs should be across from your eyes.

1 - Tree Pose: Stay as long as possible. Note: do on one leg then on another.

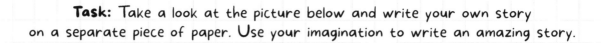

STORY

Task: Take a look at the picture below and write your own story on a separate piece of paper. Use your imagination to write an amazing story.

WeeK 8

OVERVIEW OF ENGLISH CONCEPTS

Different Formats & Media

When you study English or Language Arts, you're usually talking about the processes of **reading**, **writing**, **and thinking**. Most often, we associate those skills with **books**, but there are many other kinds of "texts" that your English skills can be applied to. In the twenty-first century, more and more different forms of expression and media are being created every day. Part of becoming a successful citizen is understanding how to apply the skills you're learning in school to new situations.

Part of being a good reader is understanding how to approach different **media**. For example, school has probably done a great job teaching you how to approach a **book**, but you probably haven't spent a lot of time thinking about how to approach a brochure or digital slideshow. Below, you'll find some tools and strategies to help you analyze and embrace media of all types!

Key Terms:
Medium: a tool or format to help communicate ideas
Media: the plural form of **medium**

Print Media
"Print Media" is a term used to describe any physical texts or documents, like a book, newspaper, magazine, brochure, flyer, etc. Print media has been around basically as long as people have been writing, but it really grew in the 1440s with the invention of the printing press. Here are some strategies that will help you break down and understand **any** piece of print media:

- Ask yourself: **Why did the creators use this medium?**
  - Why is this an appropriate place for a book, essay, pamphlet, brochure, etc?
  - Knowing this will help you understand the **author's goals and intentions better.**
- Study how the content is broken up into **sections, chapters, or headings**
  - All media should **present ideas clearly.** So, by studying the way a piece is organized, you can get at the main ideas quickly, regardless of format.
- Study any **photographs, illustrations, graphs,** or **charts** provided
  - These will usually be related to the parts of the text the author wants you to **pay the closest attention to.**

Digital Media

"Digital Media" refers to any type of text or content that is primarily published and distributed using computers and the internet. Websites, ebooks, computerized slideshows, and even multimedia videos are all examples of digital media. Here are some strategies you can use to approach any piece of digital media in an empowered way:

- Think about how the media was **distributed**
  - By thinking about which websites, organizations, or companies created the piece, you can gain insights as to its goal or purpose
  - Ask yourself: **How did I learn about this?** Did you find the content through social media, in another article you read, in a newsletter, etc.?
- Look at what **other content** the piece is **linking to**
  - What kind of articles, videos, or web sites does the author want you to see or think about?
  - Why were these links chosen, and how do they relate to the content of the text?
- Apply the **same thinking skills** we talked about for print media
  - Study any **illustrations or graphics**
  - Keep an eye on their methods of **organization**
  - Think about **why a given medium** was chosen.

From "Sense and Sensibility"

By Jane Austen

(Continued from Week 7's passages. This passage focuses on **Mr. John Dashwood, the son of Henry Dashwood**, who was the main character in Week 7's passages.)

Mr. John Dashwood had not the strong feelings of the rest of the family; but he was affected by a recommendation of such a nature at such a time, and he promised to do everything in his power to make them comfortable. His father was rendered easy by such an assurance, and Mr. John Dashwood had then leisure to consider how much there might prudently be in his power to do for them.

He was not an ill-disposed young man, unless to be rather cold hearted and rather selfish is to be ill-disposed: but he was, in general, well respected; for he conducted himself with propriety in the discharge of his ordinary duties. Had he married a more amiable woman, he might have been made still more respectable than he was: — he might even have been made amiable himself; for he was very young when he married, and very fond of his wife. But Mrs. John Dashwood was a strong caricature of himself; — more narrow-minded and selfish.

When he gave his promise to his father, he meditated within himself to increase the fortunes of his sisters by the present of a thousand pounds a-piece. "He then really thought himself equal to it. The prospect of four thousand a-year, in addition to his present income, besides the remaining half of his own mother's fortune, warmed his heart, and made him feel capable of generosity.— "Yes, he would give them three thousand pounds: it would be liberal and handsome! It would be enough to make them completely easy. Three thousand pounds! he could spare so considerable a sum with little inconvenience." — He thought of it all day long, and for many days successively, and he did not repent.

1. Based on the passage, describe **John Dashwood's** personality:

_____

_____

2. Based on the passage, describe **Mrs. John Dashwood's** personality:

_____

_____

3. In Paragraph 1, when John Dashwood "promised to do everything in his power to make **them** comfortable," who are the people Dashwood wants to make comfortable?

    A. His father and grandfather
    B. His son and wife
    C. His sisters
    D. Himself and his wife

4. What was John's **original plan**?

    A. To give his sisters nothing
    B. To take the 1,000 pounds each of his sisters got for himself
    C. To give his sisters 3,000 pounds each
    D. To give his sisters 1,000 pounds each

5. Based on what you read in the passage, make a **prediction** about what might happen next. Do you think John will wind up giving his sisters the money as planned or not? What makes you think so?

_____

_____

_____

_____

_____

Approaching Print Media

Directions: Find either a **newspaper or magazine in print form**. (Be sure it is a physical copy and **not digital/online media!**) Select two articles from the newspaper or magazine, read them, and answer the questions below to help you think about both the content of the article and the way it's presented in terms of format or media.

1. **Headline 1:** _____

    • What's going on in this article? _____

    _____

    • Is the author trying to convince you of anything or just communicating information?

    _____

    _____

    • Are there any **pictures**, **charts**, **or graphics** that accompany this article? If so, describe them here:

    _____

    _____

    • How is the article **organized**? Are there subheadings, sections, chapters, etc.? If there aren't, do the paragraphs have specific focuses?

    _____

    _____

    • How might this article be **different** if it was a piece of digital (computerized/online) media instead of a print article?

    _____

    _____

2. Headline 2: _____

   - What's going on in this article? _____
   _____

   - Is the author trying to convince you of anything or just communicating information?
   _____
   _____

   - Are there any **pictures**, **charts**, **or graphics** that accompany this article? If so, describe them here:
   _____
   _____

- How is the article **organized**? Are there subheadings, sections, chapters, etc.? If there aren't, do the paragraphs have specific focuses?

  _____

  _____

- How might this article be **different** if it was a piece of digital (computerized/online) media instead of a print article?

  _____

  _____

fitness

Please be aware of your environment and be safe at all times. If you cannot do an exercise, just try your best.

Repeat these **exercises** **4 ROUNDS**

1 - Abs: 20 times

2 - Lunges: 8 times to each leg. Note: Use your body weight or books as weight to do leg lunges.

3 - Plank: 20 sec.

4 - Run: 50m Note: Run 25 meters to one side and 25 meters back to the starting position.

From "Sense and Sensibility"

By Jane Austen

(Continued from Day 1's Passage)

No sooner was his father's funeral over, than Mrs. John Dashwood, without sending any notice of her intention to her mother-in-law, arrived with her child and their attendants. No one could dispute her right to come; the house was her husband's from the moment of his father's decease; but the indelicacy of her conduct was so much the greater, and to a woman in Mrs. Henry Dashwood's situation, with only common feelings, must have been highly unpleasing; — but in HER mind there was a sense of honor so keen, a generosity so romantic, that any offence of the kind, by whomsoever given or received, was to her a source of immovable disgust. Mrs. John Dashwood had never been a favorite with any of her husband's family; but she had had no opportunity, till the present, of showing them with how little attention to the comfort of other people she could act when occasion required it.

So acutely did Mrs. Henry Dashwood feel this ungracious behavior, and so earnestly did she despise her daughter-in-law for it, that, on the arrival of the latter, she would have quitted the house for ever, had not the entreaty of her eldest girl induced her first to reflect on the propriety of going, and her own tender love for all her three children determined her afterwards to stay, and for their sakes avoid a breach with their brother.

Elinor, this eldest daughter, whose advice was so effectual, possessed a strength of understanding, and coolness of judgment, which qualified her, though only nineteen, to be the counsellor of her mother, and enabled her frequently to counteract, to the advantage of them all, that eagerness of mind in Mrs. Dashwood which must generally have led to imprudence. She had an excellent heart; — her disposition was affectionate, and her feelings were strong; but she knew how to govern them: it was a knowledge which her mother had yet to learn; and which one of her sisters had resolved never to be taught.

Marianne's abilities were, in many respects, quite equal to Elinor's. She was sensible and clever; but eager in everything: her sorrows, her joys, could have no moderation. She was generous, amiable, interesting: she was everything but prudent. The resemblance between her and her mother was strikingly great.

Elinor saw, with concern, the excess of her sister's sensibility; but by Mrs. Dashwood it was valued and cherished. They encouraged each other now in the violence of their affliction. The agony of grief which overpowered them at first, was voluntarily renewed, was sought for, was created again and again. They gave themselves up wholly to their sorrow, seeking increase of wretchedness in every reflection that could afford it, and resolved against ever admitting consolation in future. Elinor, too, was deeply afflicted; but still she could struggle, she could exert herself. She could consult with her brother, could receive her sister-in-law on her arrival, and treat her with proper attention; and could strive to rouse her mother to similar exertion, and encourage her to similar forbearance.

Margaret, the other sister, was a good-humored, well-disposed girl; but as she had already imbibed a good deal of Marianne's romance, without having much of her sense, she did not, at thirteen, bid fair to equal her sisters at a more advanced period of life.

1. Describe the relationship between **Henry Dashwood's wife** and **John Dashwood's wife:**

_____

_____

2. Why are Mrs. Henry Dashwood and her three daughters unable to express their extreme frustration with Mrs. John Dashwood?

_____

_____

3. According to the text, how is Elinor different from her mother?

A. Elinor is rude, while her mother is kind.
B. Elinor has trouble controlling her emotions, which her mother is good at.
C. Elinor is good at controlling her emotions, which her mother has trouble with.
D. Elinor is kind, while her mother is rude.

4. Which sister is described as having a strong resemblance to Mrs. Henry Dashwood?

A. Elinor
B. Marianne
C. Margaret
D. None of them look like their mother

5. If you were in Mrs. Henry Dashwood and her daughters' position, **how would you handle this situation?** What would you say or do to John and his wife?

_____

_____

_____

_____

Approaching Digital Media

Directions: Go to one of your favorite news or entertainment websites and read/view two different pieces of digital media or content (they could be articles, videos, podcasts, etc.). After you've reviewed both pieces of digital media, answer the questions below to help you think about both the content and structure of the media you consumed.

1. **Media Piece 1:** _____

   - What's going on in this piece of media?_____
   _____

   - What do you think were the author's **goals** when they created this piece of media?
   _____
   _____

   - What **visuals** were included in this media (pictures, video, etc):
   _____
   _____

   - How is the media **organized**? Are there subheadings, sections, chapters, etc.? If there aren't, do the paragraphs have specific focuses?
   _____
   _____

   - How might this article be **different** if it was a piece of print (physical) media instead of digital media?
   _____
   _____

2.   **Media Piece 2:** _____

- What's going on in this piece of media? _____

  _____

- What do you think were the author's **goals** when they created this piece of media?

  _____

  _____

- What **visuals** were included in this media (pictures, video, etc):

  _____

  _____

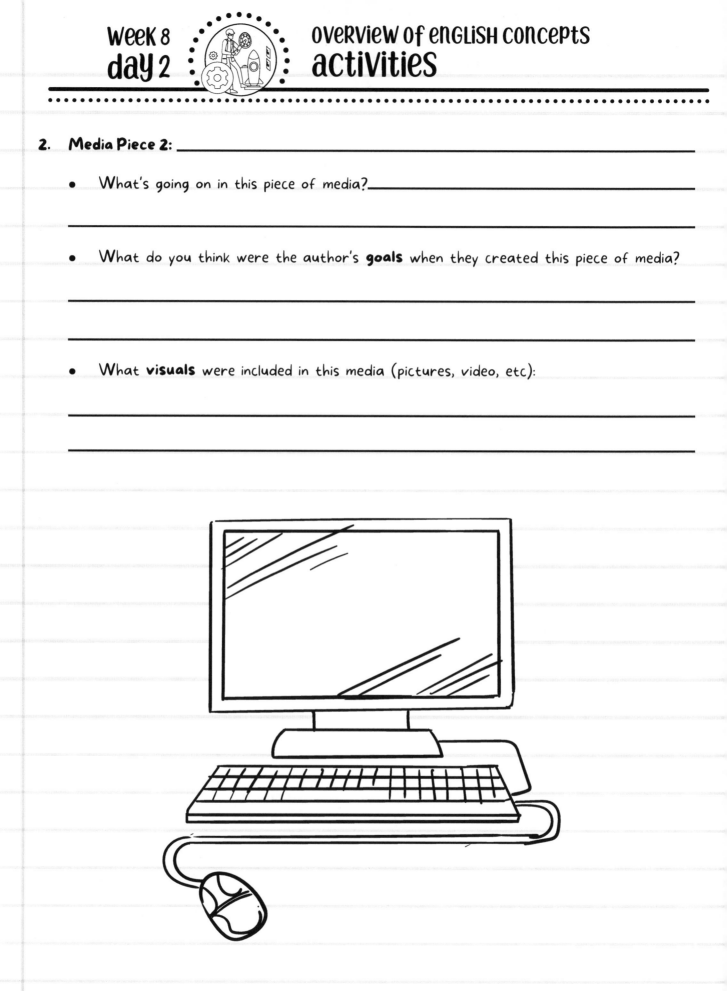

- How is the media **organized**? Are there subheadings, sections, chapters, etc.? If there aren't, do the paragraphs have specific focuses?

_____

_____

- How might this article be **different** if it was a piece of print (physical) media instead of digital media?

_____

_____

fitness

Please be aware of your environment and be safe at all times. If you cannot do an exercise, just try your best.

Repeat these **exercises** **4 ROUNDS**

2 - Side Bending: 15 times to each side. Note: try to touch your feet.

1 - Squats: 20 times. Note: imagine you are trying to sit on a chair.

3 - Tree Pose: Stay as long as possible. Note: do the same with the other leg.

Geometry

1. If a rectangle is drawn on the coordinate plane with a length of 6 units and a height of 12 units and two points are on (2,7) and (8,7), which point could be a part of the rectangle?

   A. (2, 5)   C. (-5, 2)
   B. (2, -5)   D. (13, 7)

2. If a rectangle is drawn on the coordinate plane with a length of 10 units and a height of 18 units and two points are on (-3,5) and (-3,-13), which point could be a part of the rectangle?

   A. (5, 7)   C. (-5, 7)
   B. (7,5)   D. (-3, -7)

3. If a rectangle is drawn on the coordinate plane with a length of 18 units and a height of 18 units and two points are on (2,-10) and (2,8), which point could be a part of the rectangle?

   A. (20, -10)   C. (-2, -8)
   B. (-20, -10)   D. (-8, 2)

4. If a rectangle is drawn on the coordinate plane with a length of 7 units and a height of 10 units and two points are on (-3,-5) and (-3,5), which point could be a part of the rectangle?

   A. (-4, -5)   C. (-4, 5)
   B. (9, 5)   D. (4, 5)

5. If a rectangle is drawn on the coordinate plane with a length of 12 units and a height of 22 units and two points are on (-7,-10) and (-7,12), which point could be a part of the rectangle?

   A. (-8, 12)   C. (5, 12)
   B. (-5, 12)   D. (-3, 12)

6. If a rectangle is drawn on the coordinate plane with a length of 22 units and a height of 13 units and two points are on (8,-15) and (30,-15), which point could be a part of the rectangle?

   A. (8, 2)   C. (-8, 2)
   B. (-8, -2)   D. (8, -2)

7. If a rectangle is drawn on the coordinate plane with a length of 20 units and a height of 21 units and two points are on (-14, 10) and (6,10), which point could be a part of the rectangle?

   A. (-14, 31)   C. (-14, -31)
   B. (14, 31)   D. (14, -31)

8. One side of a rectangle on the coordinate plane has a length of 26 units. If one point of the side is on (-11,-6), which point could be the other vertex?

   A. (37, -6)   C. (-37, -6)
   B. (-37, 6)   D. (37, 6)

9. One side of a rectangle on the coordinate plane has a length of 5 units. If one point of the side is on (-11,7), which point could be the other vertex?

   A. (-4, 7)   C. (-6, 7)
   B. (-4, -7)   D. (16, 7)

10. One side of a rectangle on the coordinate plane has a length of 11 units. If one point of the side is on (3,15), which point could be the other vertex?

   A. (15, 14)   C. (-14, 15)
   B. (14, 15)   D. (-9, 15)

11. One side of a rectangle on the coordinate plane has a length of 15 units. If one point of the side is on (4,-10), which point could be the other vertex?

   A. (-19, 10)   C. (-19, -10)
   B. (9, 10)   D. (19, -10)

12. One side of a rectangle on the coordinate plane has a length of 8 units. If one point of the side is on (9,19), which point could be the other vertex?

   A. (1, 19)   C. (-1, 19)
   B. (16, 19)   D. (1, 24)

13. One side of a rectangle on the coordinate plane has a length of 4 units. If one point of the side is on (-16,8), which point could be the other vertex?

   A. (0, -8)   C. (12, 8)
   B. (-8, 8)   D. (-12, 8)

14. One side of a rectangle on the coordinate plane has a length of 9 units. If one point of the side is on (-15,-12), which point could be the other vertex?

   A. (15, 12)   C. (6, -12)
   B. (-6, -12)   D. (-22, -12)

15. One side of a rectangle on the coordinate plane has a length of 3 units. If one point of the side is on (6,-2), which point could be the other vertex?

   A. (6, 1)   C. (6, 5)
   B. (6, 14)   D. (6, 10)

fitness

Please be aware of your environment and be safe at all times. If you cannot do an exercise, just try your best.

Repeat these exercises 4 ROUNDS

1 - Bend forward: 15 times.
Note: try to touch your feet. Make sure to keep your back straight and if needed you can bend your knees.

2 - Lunges: 12 times to each leg.
Note: Use your body weight or books as weight to do leg lunges.

3 - Plank: 20 sec.

4 - Abs: 20 times

Geometry

1. Which shape would be a part of the net of the following shape?

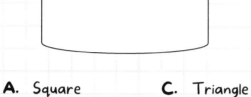

A. Square   **C.** Triangle
B. Circle   **D.** Pentagon

2. Which shape would be a part of the net of the following shape?

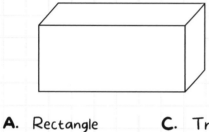

A. Rectangle   **C.** Triangle
B. Circle   **D.** Oval

3. Which shape would be a part of the net of the following shape?

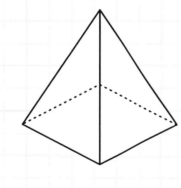

A. Circle   **C.** Triangle
B. Oval   **D.** Rectangle

4. Which shape would not be a part of the net of the following shape?

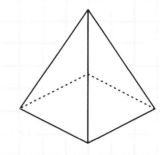

A. Isosceles Triangle
B. Scalene Triangle
C. Square

5. Which shape would not be a part of the net of the following shape?

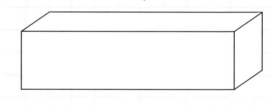

A. Square
B. Rectangle
C. Circle
D. Parallelogram

6. Which shape would not be a part of the net of the following shape?

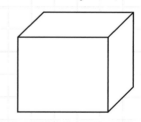

A. Triangle
B. Square
C. Rhombus
D. Quadrilateral

MatH

7. What is the surface area of a rectangular prism with a length of 4, height of 8 and width of 6?

   A. 96   C. 104
   B. 192   D. 208

8. What is the surface area of a square pyramid with a base length of 11 and a triangular height of 14?

   A. 308   C. 154
   B. 429   D. 616

9. What is the surface area of a cube with a base of 15?

   A. 225   C. 675
   B. 45   D. 1350

10. If the surface area of a cube is 2646, what is the area of one side?

    A. 25   C. 441
    B. 225   D. 21

11. If the surface area of a cube is 1536, what is the area of one side?

    A. 256   C. 526
    B. 16   D. 688

12. If the surface area of a cube is 384, what is the area of one side?

    A. 128   C. 8
    B. 32   D. 64

13. If the surface area of a cube is 150, what is the length of one side?

    A. 625   C. 5
    B. 49   D. 25

14. If the surface area of a cube is 486, what is the length of one side?

    A. 45   C. 9
    B. 405   D. 81

15. If the surface area of a cube is 1014, what is the length of one side?

    A. 45   C. 13
    B. 130   D. 169

fitness

Please be aware of your environment and be safe at all times. If you cannot do an exercise, just try your best.

Repeat these **exercises 4 ROUNDS**

1 - High Plank: 25 sec.

3 - Waist Hooping: 20 times. Note: if you do not have a hoop, pretend you have an imaginary hoop and rotate your hips 10 times.

2 - Chair: 20 sec. Note: sit on an imaginary chair, keep your back straight.

4 - Abs: 25 times

MatH

Geometry

1. A rectangle is graphed on the coordinate plane. The vertices of the rectangle are (4,6), (4,-6), (-10, -6) and (-10,6). What is a possible length for one of the sides of the rectangle?

   A. 14   C. 18
   B. 16   D. 20

2. A rectangle is graphed on the coordinate plane. The vertices of the rectangle are (-2,7), (2,7), (-2, -7) and (-2, 7). What is a possible length for one of the sides of the rectangle?

   A. 5   C. 3
   B. 4   D. 2

3. A rectangle is graphed on the coordinate plane. The vertices of the rectangle are (-9,15), (10,15), (-9, -20) and (10,-20). What is a possible length for one of the sides of the rectangle?

   A. 15   C. 25
   B. 19   D. 30

4. A rectangle is graphed on the coordinate plane. The vertices of the rectangle are (-9,3), (9,3), (-9, -5) and (9,-5). What is the area of the rectangle?

   A. 92   C. 104
   B. 96   D. 144

5. A rectangle is graphed on the coordinate plane. The vertices of the rectangle are (-3,10), (8,10), (8, -17) and (-3,-17). What is the area of the rectangle?

   A. 191   C. 170
   B. 264   D. 297

6. A rectangle is graphed on the coordinate plane. The vertices of the rectangle are (-6,11), (7,11), (-6, -4) and (7,-4). What is the area of the rectangle?

   A. 170   C. 195
   B. 185   D. 205

7. A rectangle is graphed on the coordinate plane. The vertices of the rectangle are (11,32), (26,32), (11, 14) and (26, 14). What is the perimeter of the rectangle?

   A. 33   C. 56
   B. 66   D. 43

8. A rectangle is graphed on the coordinate plane. The vertices of the rectangle are (9,-39), (9,-45), (7, -45) and (7,-39). What is the perimeter of the rectangle?

   A. 14   C. 16
   B. 12   D. 18

9. A rectangle is graphed on the coordinate plane. The vertices of the rectangle are (-25,14), (-25,8), (-16, 14) and (-16,8). What is the perimeter of the rectangle?

   A. 30   C. 60
   B. 32   D. 64

10. Alicia built a square pyramid for her history class and wants to cover it with gold paint. If the base of the pyramid is 10 inches long and the sides have a triangle height of 8 inches, how much surface area does she need to cover with paint?

    A. 110   C. 240
    B. 220   D. 260

11. Marla has a box that she would like to cover with wrapping paper. If the box is a cube and one side is 7.5 inches long, what is the total area she has to cover with wrapping paper?

- A. 311.5
- B. 317.5
- C. 337.5
- D. 357.5

12. Steve and Ted each have a rectangular prism. If Steve's prism has a base of 11 cm by 7 cm and Ted's prism has a base of 8.5 cm by 9 cm and both prisms have a height of 6 cm, what is the surface area of Steve's prism?

- A. 330
- B. 370
- C. 400
- D. 420

13. Steve and Ted each have a rectangular prism. If Steve's prism has a base of 11 cm by 7 cm and Ted's prism has a base of 8.5 cm by 9 cm and both prisms have a height of 6 cm, what is the surface area of Ted's prism?

- A. 363
- B. 383
- C. 403
- D. 413

14. Steve and Ted each have a solid rectangular prism. If Steve's prism has a base of 11 cm by 7 cm and Ted's prism has a base of 8.5 cm by 9 cm and both prisms have a height of 6 cm, which prism would require more material to construct?

- A. Require the same
- B. Need more information
- C. Ted's
- D. Steve's

15. Michelle bakes a rectangular cake that is 8 inches wide, 13 inches long and 3 inches high. She removes it from the pan to frost it. The cake is frosted on the top and the sides. How many square inches of frosting will she need?

- A. 334
- B. 230
- C. 312
- D. 167

yoga

Please be aware of your environment and be safe at all times. If you cannot do an exercise, just try your best.

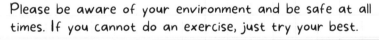

1 - **Down Dog:** 30 sec.

2 - **Bend Down:** 30 sec.

3 - **Chair:** 30 sec.

4 - **Child Pose:** 30 sec.

5 - **Shavasana:** as long as you can. Note: think of happy moments and relax your mind.

experiment

The Lifecycle of Ferns

By now, you've probably learned or observed how most plants grow from seeds that are spread by animals. A few plants out there, however, find other, more unique ways to reproduce in the wild. One perfect (and commonplace) example is the **fern**. Ferns spread using **spores**, which is actually much more like the way a fungus spreads than the reproduction process of most plants.

Fern spores generally grow and develop over the summer and into the early fall, which makes this the perfect time to get up close and personal with a fern to observe its growth and development. This activity will involve purchasing and caring for a fern. This is **a big responsibility**, as the plant is a living thing (and also probably not free!). You'll observe your fern carefully over a period of a few weeks to practice your scientific skills and then continue to care for it as long as you like!

Materials:

- I live potted fern or hanging fern basket from the garden center
- I watering can
- Access to cool running water
- I pair of pruning shears or heavy-duty scissors
- I digital camera (a cell phone camera works perfectly)
- Internet access (for research)
- A magnifying glass
- Art supplies (markers, colored pencils, etc.)
- Notepaper

Procedure:

1. As soon as you bring your live fern home from the garden center, grab your notepaper and magnifying glass to create a brief, but in-depth, description of the fern. Describe what it looks like using **words** and be sure to describe each individual part of the plant, studying it up close using your magnifying glass. (If you have trouble naming the different parts of the fern, feel free to do some internet research to learn more about the names of plant parts.)

2. Using your art supplies, draw a picture of both the top and undersides of the fern's leaves on your notepaper as well.

3. Place the fern in a shady (but not dark) area and water it if the soil feels dry.

4. Using your camera, take a picture of the fern on its first day in its new environment.

5. Over the next few days and weeks, be sure to water the fern anytime the soil begins to feel dry (but do not over-water it or soak the soil). Every two or three days, check the fern for dried up or off-colored parts that need to be removed. Each time you see one, make note of the date in your notes, describe the area that needs to be removed using words, take a picture with your digital camera, and then carefully trim it off using pruning shears or scissors. (If you have questions or concerns about your fern's health or growth, use the internet to connect with some great resources about fern care.)

6. Every time you water or prune your fern, look on the underside of the leaves to check the development of the round spores that grow there. Be careful not to disturb the spores but be sure to photograph them occasionally to track their development. Whenever you notice the fern change or grow, be sure to document it in your notes and using your camera.

7. After a few weeks of monitoring your fern carefully, answer the questions below. Once you've done that, you do not need to officially monitor the fern any longer.

8. Continue to care for your fern with watering and pruning.

Follow-Up Questions:

1. How did your fern **change** or grow **between** the time you brought it home and the end of your observation period?

_____

_____

_____

2. How do you think the process of fern growth might be different **in the wild** where a person was not caring for the plant?

_____

_____

_____

yoga

Please be aware of your environment and be safe at all times. If you cannot do an exercise, just try your best.

3 - Stretching: Stay as long as possible. Note: do on one leg then on another.

2 - Down Dog: 30 sec.

4 - Lower Plank: 20 sec. Note: Keep your back straight and body tight.

6 - Shavasana: 5 min. Note: this pose is very important and provides you with long term benefits. Try not to skip this. Close your eyes and imagine who you want to be and what your goals are! Always think happy thoughts.

1 - Tree Pose: Stay as long as possible. Note: do on one leg then on another.

5 - Book Pose: 20 sec. Note: Keep your core tight. Legs should be across from your eyes.

Task: Take a look at the first four images. Which pictures (5 - 10) can be created using any of the patterns in the first four images?

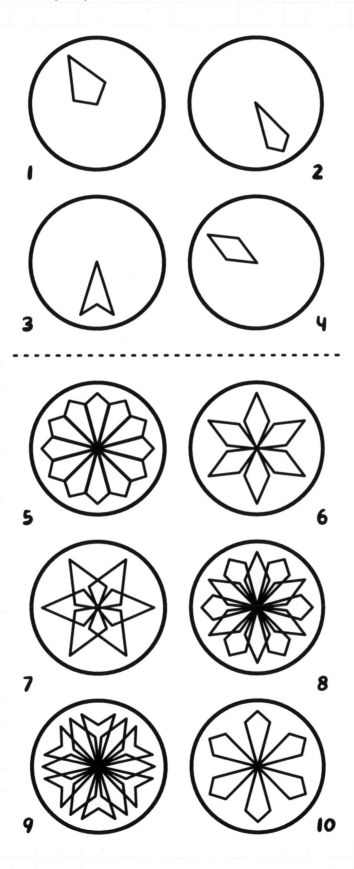

week 9

Point of View (in Non-Fiction)

Throughout the summer, we've talked about different ways to approach and think about a text. We've looked at things very closely one sentence at a time, and we've learned how to notice and articulate the relationships between ideas to demonstrate comprehension and discuss what we've read in a high-level way. One aspect of texts that we haven't discussed yet, however, is **point of view**.

Every text is written from a particular **point of view**, which is to say, it has a certain **perspective**. In non-fiction and informational texts, understanding the author's or text's **point of view** is crucial to getting a full sense of what is being communicated. Two authors can write about the identical topic or event, but their different points of view will result in completely different texts.

Key Terms:
Point of View: The perspective that the author is writing from
Perspective: An attitude, set of beliefs, or worldview that influences the way you approach life and the world
Bias: A strong preference for certain beliefs or ideas that causes an author to belittle or unfairly judge different points of view
Biased: A text or author that shows **bias**

Questions to Ask Yourself when Reading Non-Fiction:
- Does the author ever **explicitly state their point of view**?
    - Generally, this will occur near the <u>beginning</u> or <u>end</u> of a text
    - Do they explain how they feel? Do they describe what aspects of their life or experience make them feel that way?
- Does the author seem to **like/enjoy/feel excited about this topic**, or does it seem like they're **skeptical of or distrustful** of the people, places, or things they're talking about?
    - The quicker you can pick this up, the easier a time you'll have comprehending the text (and its point of view) on the whole
- What does this author's point of view provide **that you might not get from other authors?**
- Does the author's point of view on this topic lead to examples of **biased** thinking or **dismissive** arguments?
    - If a text seems **biased or slanted** in any way, it's extra important to consider the author's point of view!

Each time you approach a new non-fiction text, finding answers to those four questions will help you gain an understanding of what the text truly says, how the author truly feels, and whether you can consider that text honest and useful.

From "Sense and Sensibility"

By Jane Austen

(Continued from last week's passages)
(**NOTE:** In this passage, "Mrs. John Dashwood" refers to John Dashwood's wife, while "Mrs. Dashwood" refers to Henry Dashwood's wife, who is also the mother of Elinor, Marianne, and Margaret.)

Mrs. John Dashwood now installed herself mistress of Norland; and her mother and sisters-in-law were degraded to the condition of visitors. As such, however, they were treated by her with quiet civility; and by her husband with as much kindness as he could feel towards anybody beyond himself, his wife, and their child. He really pressed them, with some earnestness, to consider Norland as their home; and, as no plan appeared so eligible to Mrs. Dashwood as remaining there till she could accommodate herself with a house in the neighborhood, his invitation was accepted.

A continuance in a place where everything reminded her of former delight, was exactly what suited her mind. In seasons of cheerfulness, no temper could be more cheerful than hers, or possess, in a greater degree, that sanguine expectation of happiness which is happiness itself. But in sorrow she must be equally carried away by her fancy, and as far beyond consolation as in pleasure she was beyond alloy.

Mrs. John Dashwood did not at all approve of what her husband intended to do for his sisters. To take three thousand pounds from the fortune of their dear little boy would be impoverishing him to the most dreadful degree. She begged him to think again on the subject. How could he answer it to himself to rob his child, and his only child too, of so large a sum? And what possible claim could the Miss Dashwoods, who were related to him only by half blood, which she considered as no relationship at all, have on his generosity to so large an amount. It was very well known that no affection was ever supposed to exist between the children of any man by different marriages; and why was he to ruin himself, and their poor little Harry, by giving away all his money to his half-sisters?

"It was my father's last request to me," replied her husband, "that I should assist his widow and daughters."

1. How does **John Dashwood** feel about his **sisters** and **step-mother** living with them?

_____

_____

2. How does **Mrs. Dashwood** (the widow) feel about continuing to live at Norland?

_____

_____

3. Which of these best describes **Mrs. John Dashwood's** point of view in the passage?

   A. Looking out for other people is highly virtuous.
   B. Family should be the most important thing in a person's life.
   C. You should look out for yourself first, then try to help other people.
   D. If you try to help others, you'll only be taking time, energy, and money away from yourself.

4. Which of these best describes **John Dashwood's** point of view in the passage?

   A. People should keep promises and honor their word.
   B. People should keep promises and honor their word unless it is inconvenient.
   C. People shouldn't worry about keeping promises or honoring their word.
   D. People shouldn't worry about keeping promises or honoring their word, except in the case of family.

5. Think **from Mrs. John Dashwood's point of view** and write a few sentences explaining how you would convince your husband that his sisters and step-mother should be gotten rid of:

_____

_____

_____

_____

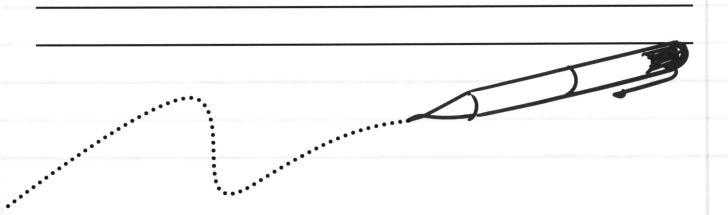

Analyzing Point of View in Nonfiction (Pt.1)

Directions: Select a piece of either digital or print **news media** (like a newspaper, magazine, or news site) and choose **two different articles or columns to read**. Read the two articles or columns and answer the questions below to think about each one in terms of **point of view**.

1. **Article Title:** _____

    *   What main ideas are being explored in this article? _____
    _____

    *   Does the author ever reveal their **point of view** in the text? If so, when, and what is that point of view? If **not**, what could you figure out or <u>infer</u> about their point of view?
    _____
    _____

    *   Does the author seem to **like/enjoy/feel excited about this topic**, or does it seem like they're **skeptical of or distrustful** of the people, places, or things they're talking about?
    _____
    _____

    *   What does this author's point of view provide **that you might not get from other authors?**
    _____
    _____

    *   Does the author's point of view on this topic lead to any examples of **biased** thinking or **dismissive** arguments?
    _____
    _____

2. **Article Title:** _____

- What main ideas are being explored in this article? _____

  _____

- Does the author ever reveal their **point of view** in the text? If so, when, and what is that point of view? If **not**, what could you figure out or infer about their point of view?

  _____

  _____

- Does the author seem to **like/enjoy/feel excited about this topic**, or does it seem like they're **skeptical of or distrustful** of the people, places, or things they're talking about?

  _____

  _____

- What does this author's point of view provide **that you might not get from other authors?**

_____

_____

- Does the author's point of view on this topic lead to any examples of **biased** thinking or **dismissive** arguments?

_____

_____

fitness

Please be aware of your environment and be safe at all times. If you cannot do an exercise, just try your best.

Repeat these **exercises 4 ROUNDS**

2 - Lunges: 8 times to each leg. Note: Use your body weight or books as weight to do leg lunges.

1 - Abs: 20 times

4 - Run: 50m Note: Run 25 meters to one side and **25** meters back to the starting position.

3 - Plank: 20 sec.

From "Sense and Sensibility"

By Jane Austen

(Continued from Day I's Passage)

"It was my father's last request to me," replied her husband, "that I should assist his widow and daughters."

"He did not know what he was talking of, I dare say; ten to one but he was light-headed at the time. Had he been in his right senses, he could not have thought of such a thing as begging you to give away half your fortune from your own child."

"He did not stipulate for any particular sum, my dear Fanny; he only requested me, in general terms, to assist them, and make their situation more comfortable than it was in his power to do. Perhaps it would have been as well if he had left it wholly to myself. He could hardly suppose I should neglect them. But as he required the promise, I could not do less than give it; at least I thought so at the time. The promise, therefore, was given, and must be performed. Something must be done for them whenever they leave Norland and settle in a new home."

"Well, then, LET something be done for them; but THAT something need not be three thousand pounds. Consider," she added, "that when the the money is once parted with, it never can return. Your sisters will marry, and it will be gone forever. If, indeed, it could be restored to our poor little boy — "

"Why, to be sure," said her husband, very gravely, "that would make great difference. The time may come when Harry will regret that so large a sum was parted with. If he should have a numerous family, for instance, it would be a very convenient addition."

"To be sure it would."

"Perhaps, then, it would be better for all parties, if the sum were diminished one half. — Five hundred pounds would be a prodigious increase to their fortunes!"

"Oh! beyond anything great! What brother on earth would do half so much for his sisters, even if REALLY his sisters! And as it is — only half blood! — But you have such a generous spirit!"

"I would not wish to do anything mean," he replied. "One had rather, on such occasions, do too much than too little. No one, at least, can think I have not done enough for them: even themselves, they can hardly expect more."

1. From John's point of view, why is his wife's suggestion that he forget about his sisters a problem?

_____

_____

2. Who is **Harry**, and how is he connected to the debate in this passage?

_____

_____

_____

3. Which of these does **not** describe how Mrs. John Dashwood feels about her husband's father's final wishes?

A. They shouldn't be obeyed because the sisters don't really count as family.
B. They shouldn't be obeyed because he was probably delirious when he made them.
C. They shouldn't be obeyed because they need to save the money for their own son.
D. They shouldn't be obeyed because the sisters are unkind to John.

4. Based on the passage, what is Mrs. John Dashwood's first name?

A. Elinor
B. Marianne
C. Fanny
D. She has no first name

5. Do you think Mrs. John Dashwood was **successful** in convincing her husband to **listen to her advice** in this passage? What makes you say that?

_____

_____

_____

_____

Analyzing Point of View in Nonfiction (Pt.2)

Directions: Select a piece of either digital or print **news media** (like a newspaper, magazine, or news site) and choose **two different articles or columns to read**. If you used a digital source on Day 1, use a print source today; if you used a print source on Day 1, try to access a digital source! Read the two articles or columns and answer the questions below to think about each one in terms of **point of view**.

1. **Article Title:** _____

   • What main ideas are being explored in this article? _____

   _____

   • Does the author ever reveal their **point of view** in the text? If so, when, and what is that point of view? If **not**, what could you figure out or <u>infer</u> about their point of view?

   _____

   _____

   • Does the author seem to **like/enjoy/feel excited about this topic**, or does it seem like they're **skeptical of or distrustful** of the people, places, or things they're talking about?

   _____

   _____

   • What does this author's point of view provide **that you might not get from other authors?**

   _____

   _____

   • Does the author's point of view on this topic lead to any examples of **biased** thinking or **dismissive** arguments?

   _____

   _____

2. **Article Title:** _____

- What main ideas are being explored in this article? _____

_____

- Does the author ever reveal their **point of view** in the text? If so, when, and what is that point of view? If **not**, what could you figure out or <u>infer</u> about their point of view?

_____

_____

- Does the author seem to **like/enjoy/feel excited about this topic**, or does it seem like they're **skeptical of or distrustful** of the people, places, or things they're talking about?

_____

_____

- What does this author's point of view provide **that you might not get from other authors?**

_____

_____

- Does the author's point of view on this topic lead to any examples of **biased** thinking or **dismissive** arguments?

_____

_____

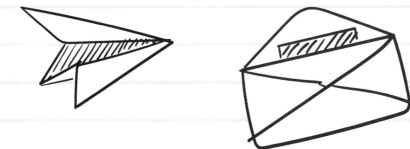

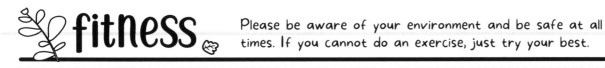

fitness

Please be aware of your environment and be safe at all times. If you cannot do an exercise, just try your best.

Repeat these **exercises 4 ROUNDS**

2 - Side Bending: 15 times to each side. Note: try to touch your feet.

1 - Squats: 20 times. Note: imagine you are trying to sit on a chair.

3 - Tree Pose: Stay as long as possible. Note: do the same with the other leg.

Statistics

1. Which set of data has a range of 12?

   A. 12, 23, 10, 19   C. 12, 23, 11, 22
   B. 12, 12, 14, 11   D. 10, 12, 14, 8

2. The mean of a set of data with a set of three data points is 27. What could the values of the three points be?

   A. 20, 47, 32   C. 22, 24, 27
   B. 26, 28, 32   D. 22, 29, 30

3. What is the median of the data set below?
   5, 6, 8, 9, 9, 10, 11

   A. 9   B. 5   C. 10   D. 8

4. What is the mode of the data set below?
   11, 14, 16, 12, 10, 10, 19, 11, 18, 11

   A. 10   B. 11   C. 14   D. 19

5. Which set of data has the least median value?

   A. 2, 4, 6, 6, 9, 11, 16
   B. 1, 1, 3, 4, 4, 6, 8
   C. 1, 1, 2, 3, 9, 11, 16
   D. 2, 3, 4, 6, 8, 9, 18

6. Which data set has a mode of 18?

   A. 16, 16, 17, 18, 19, 21
   B. 12, 12, 12, 17, 18
   C. 12, 13, 13, 21, 29, 30
   D. 11, 16, 18, 18, 22, 26

7. What is the mean of the data below?
   42, 44, 49, 52, 58

   A. 44   C. 46
   B. 42   D. 49

8. What is the range of the data below?
   21, 22, 27, 28, 29, 29,

   A. 8   C. 29
   B. 27   D. 21

9. Which description of the data set below is approximately 14?
   10, 12, 13, 13, 14, 16, 18

   A. Median   C. Mode
   B. Mean   D. Range

10. Which description of the data set below is equal to 20?
    8, 20, 20, 23, 28, 31, 32

    A. Median   C. Mode
    B. Mean   D. Range

11. Mr. Lawrence recorded for the last seven years the number of students in his classes who owned cell phones. The mean was 16 and the median was 18. Which data set could represent his sample?

    A. 5, 12, 15, 18, 19, 21, 22
    B. 12, 14, 15, 18, 19, 21, 22
    C. 10, 12, 15, 19, 19, 21, 22
    D. 12, 12, 16, 19, 19, 21, 22

12. Nicole's last 5 science scores were 72, 91, 86, 100 and 83. If her sixth test score was a 93, which of the following is a true statement?

A. Her range increased after the sixth test.
B. Her range decreased after the sixth test.
C. Her mean fell in value after the sixth test.
D. Her mean rose in value after the sixth test.

13. The heights of the starting players on a basketball team are 71 inches, 71 inches, 79 inches, 75 inches and 76 inches. Which statement does not describe the heights of these players?

A. The mode of the team is 71 inches.
B. The range of the team is 8 inches.
C. The mean height of the team is 73 inches.
D. The median height of the team is 75 inches.

14. Morgan swam laps at the pool every day for a week. He sawm the following laps: 42, 26, 9, 11, 35. Which of the following is a true statement?

A. The range of his data set is 33.
B. The mode of his data set is 9.
C. The mean of his data set is 26.
D. The median of his data set is 24.6.

15. Shannon counted the number of flowers by type in her yard. She made the following statements about her data: the mode of the numbers is smaller than the range. The median of her data is 11. Which could have been her data set?

A. 6, 6, 9, 10, 11, 14, 18
B. 6, 6, 9, 11, 14, 15, 18
C. 6, 9, 10, 11, 14, 14, 18
D. 6, 10, 10, 10, 11, 14, 14

fitness

Please be aware of your environment and be safe at all times. If you cannot do an exercise, just try your best.

Repeat these exercises **4 ROUNDS**

2 - Lunges: 12 times to each leg. Note: Use your body weight or books as weight to do leg lunges.

3 - Plank: 20 sec.

1 - Bend forward: 15 times. Note: try to touch your feet. Make sure to keep your back straight and if needed you can bend your knees.

4 - Abs: 20 times

Statistics

Use the line plot below to answer questions 1-4.

Use the line plot below to answer the following questions.

1. What is the mean of the data?

    A. 7   C. 6.4
    B. 6.8   D. 6

2. What is the mode of the data?

    A. 9   C. 5
    B. 7   D. 6

3. What is the range of the data?

    A. 3   C. 5
    B. 4   D. 6

4. What is the median of the data?

    A. 7   C. 9
    B. 8   D. 10

5. What is the mean of the data?

    A. 7   C. 9
    B. 6   D. 8

6. Where does a gap occur in the data?

    A. 6   C. 10
    B. 8   D. 12

7. What is the range of the data?

    A. 6   C. 17
    B. 8   D. 7

8. What is the median of the data?

    A. 6   C. 8
    B. 7   D. 9

Use the line plot below to answer the following questions.

MatH

9. What is the mode of the data?

   A. 1   C. 5
   B. 4   D. 6

10. What is the median of the data?

    A. 3   C. 5
    B. 1   D. 4

11. What is the mean of the data?

    A. 2   C. 4
    B. 3   D. 5

12. What is the range of the data?

    A. 5   C. 4
    B. 6   D. 3

13. Use the data below to create a line plot.

    15, 12, 15, 15, 14, 9, 12, 12, 15, 11

14. Use your line plot to calculate the mode of the data.

    _____

15. Use your line plot to calculate the median of the data.

    _____

fitness

Please be aware of your environment and be safe at all times. If you cannot do an exercise, just try your best.

Repeat these **exercises 4 ROUNDS**

1 - High Plank: 25 sec.

2 - Chair: 20 sec. Note: sit on an imaginary chair, keep your back straight.

3 - Waist Hooping: 20 times. Note: if you do not have a hoop, pretend you have an imaginary hoop and rotate your hips 10 times.

4 - Abs: 25 times

Statistics

Use the graph below to answer questions 1-4.

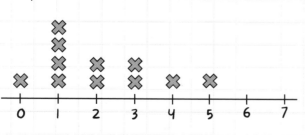

2   3   4   5   6   7   8

1.   What is the median of the data?

   A. 4   C. 6
   B. 5   D. 7

2.   What is the range of the data?

   A. 5   C. 7
   B. 6   D. 8

3.   What is the mean of the data?

   A. 3   C. 5
   B. 4   D. 6

4.   What is the mean absolute variation to the nearest tenth?

   A. 1.8   C. 2.1
   B. 1.9   D. 2.3

Use the line plot below to answer questions 5-8.

0   1   2   3   4   5   6   7

5.   What is the first quartile?

   A. 4   C. 2
   B. 3   D. 1

6.   What is the median?

   A. 2   C. 4
   B. 3   D. 5

7.   What is the third quartile?

   A. 2   C. 4
   B. 3   D. 5

8.   What is the interquartile range?

   A. 1   C. 4
   B. 2   D. 3

9.   A set of data has the following measures: Third quartile is 18 and interquartile range is 6.

   What is the first quartile?

   A. 12   C. 20
   B. 14   D. 24

Use the graph below to calculate the answers for questions 10-13.

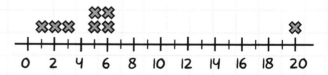

0   2   4   6   8   10   12   14   16   18   20

10. What is the mean of the data?

   A. 5   C. 1
   B. 6   D. 20

11. What is the median of the data?

   A. 5   C. 7
   B. 6   D. 8

12. What is the range of the data?

   A. 17   C. 19
   B. 18   D. 20

13. What is the mean absolute deviation of the data?

   A. 2.6   C. 3.2
   B. 2.8   D. 3.5

14. What is the interquartile range of the following data set?

   12, 15, 16, 17, 18, 21, 23

   A. 15   C. 21
   B. 6   D. 8

15. What is the interquartile range of the following data set?

   20, 25, 40, 50, 100, 25, 125, 50

   A. 50   C. 75
   B. 25   D. 100

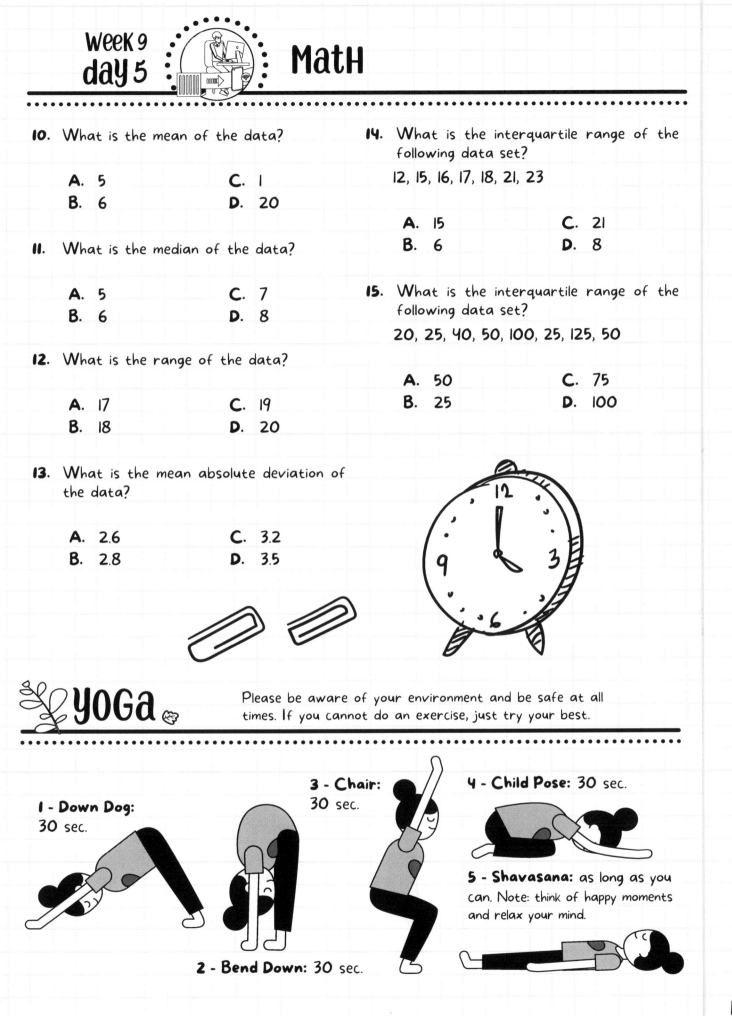

yoga

Please be aware of your environment and be safe at all times. If you cannot do an exercise, just try your best.

1 - Down Dog: 30 sec.

2 - Bend Down: 30 sec.

3 - Chair: 30 sec.

4 - Child Pose: 30 sec.

5 - Shavasana: as long as you can. Note: think of happy moments and relax your mind.

experiment

Fossil Formation

Recently, you've gotten to know **ferns** *pretty well! Did you know that ferns like the ones you've been taking care of have existed on this planet since at least the time of the dinosaurs? One of the ways we know that is by studying* **fossils**. *Fossils are impressions made by the ancient remains of plants and animals which have hardened into stone over millions of years.*

This week, you'll be playing with your food to create a model of **how fossils are formed** *over many millions of years. Luckily, we'll be compressing that into just a weekend!*

Materials:

- 3 different colored or textured slices of bread (for example, one white, one wheat, one sourdough)
- Some gummy candies (fish, worms, octopi, etc.)
- A dishtowel
- A large drinking straw or piece of small PVC pipe
- A magnifying glass
- Something flat and heavy (like a couple of big books or a baking sheet with a few dumbbells on top of it)
- Notepaper

Procedure:

1. Carefully remove the crusts from all three slices of bread, leaving as much of the center as possible.

2. Lay out your dishtowel perfectly flat and place one slice of the bread (whichever is squishiest in texture is best) in the very middle of it. This represents the ground about 65 million years ago, when the dinosaurs lived.

3. Place a few of your gummy candies on top of the slice of bread to represent plants and animals from the time of the dinosaurs.

4. Take a second slice of bread and press it down on top of the gummy candies you've placed, creating a sort of sandwich. This slice represents new soil, which was created by volcanic activity, changes in ocean level, and other natural processes over time.

experiment

5. Place some more gummy candies on top of the second slice of bread. These represent plants and animals that lived during the Ice Age, about 2.6 million years ago.

6. Place your third piece of bread on top of the layer of gummies and press down firmly. You should now have a two-layer sandwich that goes: bread, gummies, bread, gummies, bread.

7. Carefully wrap your dishtowel around the "sandwich" as tightly as possible. Place the bundle you've just created somewhere out of the way, where it can stay for a few days, and put your heavy objects on top of it (**Remember**, you want to <u>flatten</u> things out, so if the heavy objects you were able to find aren't flat, place them on top of something like a baking sheet to provide even pressure). This pressure is how we're going to accelerate the fossil formation process from millions of years to just a few nights.

8. Leave your fossil sandwich wrapped and under pressure for at least 48 hours.

9. Carefully remove the weight from the top of your fossil sandwich and gently unwrap the dishtowel to get to the bread layers.

10. Poke your straw or PVC pipe down into the sandwich, pressing until you feel the tabletop or counter beneath. Pull the straw upward and gently squeeze out its contents (if you're using a clear straw, you can just view them directly in there). Describe what you see in your notes. How have the bread and pieces of gummy candy changed since the last time you saw them?

11. Try to peel the layers of your sandwich apart and describe how it feels to do so in your notes.

12. Once you've exposed the "Ice Age" layer, study the gummy candies and their effect on the bread around them. Notice both the "fossil" impressions being created on the bread and the way the time and pressure have changed the gummies themselves.

13. Peel down to the "Dinosaur" layer, and study the gummy candies and their effect on the bread around them. Notice both the "fossil" impressions being created on the bread and the way the time and pressure have changed the gummies themselves.

14. Answer the questions below; then clean up your materials.

Follow-Up Questions:

1. Based on this activity, how is the **ground below us** actually made of many different layers?

_____

_____

_____

2. How did **pressure** act like **time** in this activity?

_____

_____

_____

 yoga

Please be aware of your environment and be safe at all times. If you cannot do an exercise, just try your best.

3 - Stretching: Stay as long as possible.
Note: do on one leg then on another.

2 - Down Dog: 30 sec.

4 - Lower Plank: 20 sec.
Note: Keep your back straight and body tight.

1 - Tree Pose: Stay as long as possible. Note: do on one leg then on another.

6 - Shavasana: 5 min.
Note: this pose is very important and provides you with long term benefits. Try not to skip this. Close your eyes and imagine who you want to be and what your goals are! Always think happy thoughts.

5 - Book Pose: 20 sec.
Note: Keep your core tight. Legs should be across from your eyes.

Task: Take a look at image 5. Which two images below would you need to produce image 5?

Hint: You can rotate any of the pieces.

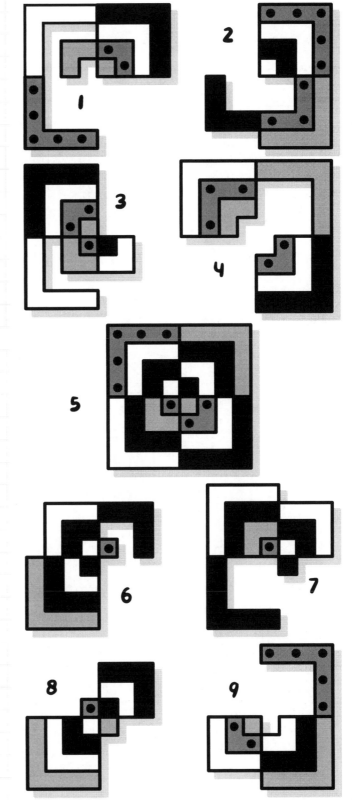

Point of View (in Fiction)

Last week, we introduced the concept of **point of view** in non-fiction. This week, we'll be stretching our thinking to talk about **fiction** as well. When we discussed non-fiction, we focused on the **author's point of view** and the way they presented ideas. When it comes to fiction, it's all about what **point of view the story is written from!**

Understanding point of view in fiction helps you comprehend the story on a deeper, more complete level. When you understand **point of view**, a story isn't just about who the characters are and what happened to them; it's about the way the story itself is crafted and presented to the reader. Today, we'll introduce some strategies and tools you can use to analyze fiction in terms of point of view.

Analyzing Fiction for Point of View

When you consume a fictional text, whether it's a novel, short story, movie, or episode of a TV show, one of the first things you should start thinking about as you read/watch/listen is **point of view!** Here are a few steps to help you orient yourself inside the text:

1. Determine if the literary text is written in <u>**first person**</u> (with the narrator using pronouns like "I," "me," and "we") or <u>**third person**</u> (with the narrator simply telling the story, but not acting as a character in it).
2. If the text has a <u>**first-person**</u> narrator, be sure you understand **who that character is** in the context of the story
   o Are they the protagonist? Are they the antagonist? Are they a side character who is observing what's going on?
3. If the text has a <u>**third-person**</u> narrator, ask yourself "Is the narrator an **impartial observer** (who doesn't judge or comment on what the characters do) or **do they interject their own voice** or opinion into the writing?"
4. Once you've identified the narrator and their style of presenting the story, think of how the narrator's point of view impacts the story
   o Which scenes or moments might be **better or more richly described** if someone else was narrating? Which scenes or moments does this narrator provide **unique insight on** that another narrator couldn't?

What about multiple narrators?!

More and more frequently, authors will write books in which different sections or chapters are narrated by different characters. This presents a unique (but fun!) challenge when you're focusing on point of view. If you encounter a book with multiple narrators...

- Take notes to keep track of who is narrating which sections of the book
- Think about the different narrators' **personalities** -- how do they view the characters and events of the story differently?
- Ask yourself <u>**why**</u> the author chose that particular character to narrate this section
- <u>When you're done with the text</u>, reflect back on why you think the author chose to tell the story through multiple points of view and what you think each narrator achieved or added to the story.

From "The Makers of Canada: Champlain"

By N.E. Dionne

In undertaking to write a biography of Samuel Champlain, the founder of Quebec and the father of New France, our only design is to make somewhat better known the dominant characteristics of the life and achievements of a man whose memory is becoming more cherished as the years roll on.

Everyone will admire Champlain's disinterested actions, his courage, his loyalty, his charity, and all those noble and magnificent qualities which are rarely found united in one individual in so prominent a degree. We cannot overpraise that self-rejection which enabled him to bear without complaint the ingratitude of many of his interpreters, and the servants of the merchants; nor can we overlook, either, the charity which he exercised towards the aborigines and new settlers; the protection which he afforded them under trying circumstances, or his zeal in promoting the honor and glory of God, and his respect for the Récollet and Jesuit fathers who honored him with their cordial friendship. His wisdom is evidenced in such a practical fact as his choice of Quebec as the capital of New France, despite the rival claims of Montreal and Three Rivers, and his numerous writings reveal him to us as a keen and sagacious observer, a man of science and a skillful and intrepid mariner. As a documenter of new territories, Champlain added yet another laurel to his crown, for he excelled all his predecessors, both by the ample volume of his descriptions and by the logical arrangement of the geographical data which he supplied. The impetus which he gave to cartographical science can scarcely be overestimated.

Naturalist, mariner, geographer, such was Samuel Champlain, and to a degree remarkable for the age in which he lived. It is, perhaps, unnecessary to dwell upon the morality of the virtuous founder. The testimony of the Hurons, who, twenty years after his death, still pointed to the life of Champlain as a model of all positive virtues, is sufficient, and it is certain that no governor under the old régime presented a more brilliant example of faith, piety, uprightness, or soundness of judgment. A brief outline of the character of Champlain has been given in order that the plan of this biography may be better understood. Let us now glance at his career more in detail.

1. How would you describe the author's **point of view** on the topic of Samuel Champlain?

_____

_____

_____

_____

2. Based on the text, what were Samuel Champlain's greatest accomplishments?

_____

_____

_____

_____

3. According to the text, which city did Champlain make the capital of New France?

- **A.** Montreal
- **B.** Quebec
- **C.** Three Rivers
- **D.** Ottowa

4. Which of Champlain's qualities does the author focus on the most?

- **A.** His wisdom and virtue
- **B.** His strength and leadership
- **C.** His handsomeness and bravery
- **D.** His ruthlessness

5. What does the sentence "It is, perhaps, unnecessary to dwell upon the morality of the virtuous founder" tell you about the author's point of view or **biases?**

_____

_____

_____

Analyzing Point of View in Fiction (Pt.1)

<u>Directions</u>: Think of one of your **favorite** works of **fiction**. It could be a book, a short story, a movie, an episode of a television show, etc. Take a few minutes to reflect on your experience with that text; then answer the questions below to help you think about point of view. **NOTE:** It may be useful to have the text with you as you work, in case you need to check anything!

I.   **Text Title:** _____

   • What happens in the text you selected? Write a short summary:

   _____

   _____

   _____

   _____

   • Is the text written in **first-** or **third-person?** Who is the narrator, if they are identified?

   _____

   _____

   • Are there any times in the story when the narrator shows **bias**, either in favor of or against any of the characters?

   _____

   _____

   • What does this narrator's point of view provide **that you might not get if someone else was the narrator?**

   _____

   _____

- Pick <u>your favorite character</u> from the story who is **not** the narrator. How would the way the story is told be **different** if your favorite character was the narrator instead?

_____

_____

_____

_____

fitness

Please be aware of your environment and be safe at all times. If you cannot do an exercise, just try your best.

Repeat these **exercises** **4 ROUNDS**

1 - Abs: 20 times

2 - Lunges: 8 times to each leg. Note: Use your body weight or books as weight to do leg lunges.

3 - Plank: 20 sec.

4 - Run: 50m Note: Run 25 meters to one side and **25** meters back to the starting position.

From "The Makers of Canada: Champlain"

By N.E. Dionne

(Continued from Day 1's Passage)

Samuel Champlain, whose parents were Antoine Champlain and Marguerite Le Roy, was born at Brouage, now Hiers Brouage, a small village in the province of Saintonge, France, in the year 1570, or according to the Biographie Saintongeoise in 1567. His parents belonged to the Catholic religion, as their first names would seem to indicate.

When quite young Samuel Champlain was entrusted to the care of the parish priest, who imparted to him the elements of education and instilled his mind with religious principles. His youth appears to have glided quietly away, spent for the most part with his family, and in assisting his father, who was a mariner, in his wanderings upon the sea. The knowledge thus obtained was of great service to him, for after a while he became not only conversant with the life of a mariner, but also with the science of geography and of astronomy. When Samuel Champlain was about twenty years of age, he tendered his services to Marshal d'Aumont, one of the chief commanders of the Catholic army in its expedition against the Huguenots.

When the League had done its work and the army was disbanded in 1598, Champlain returned to Brouage, and sought a favorable opportunity to advance his fortune in a manner more agreeable, if possible, to his tastes, and more compatible with his abilities. In the meantime Champlain did not remain idle, for he resolved to find the means of making a voyage to Spain in order "to acquire and cultivate acquaintance, and make a true report to His Majesty (Henry IV) of the particularities which could not be known to any Frenchmen, for the reason that they have not free access there." He left Blavet at the beginning of the month of August, and ten days after he arrived near Cape Finisterre. Having remained for six days at the Isle of Bayona, in Galicia, he proceeded towards San Lucar de Barameda, which is at the mouth of the river Seville, where he remained for three months. During this time he went to Seville and made surveys of the place. While Champlain was at Seville, a patache, or advice boat, arrived from Puerto Rico bearing a communication addressed to the king of Spain, informing him that a portion of the English army had put out to sea with the intention of attacking Puerto Rico.

The king fitted out twenty ships to oppose the English, one of which, the Saint Julien, was commanded by Provençal, Champlain's uncle. Champlain proposed to join the expedition under his uncle, but Provençal was ordered elsewhere, and General Soubriago offered the command of the Saint Julien to Champlain, which he gladly accepted.

1. Based on the passage, how would you describe **Champlain** in his <u>youth</u>?

_____

_____

_____

_____

2. According to the <u>text</u>, why did Champlain originally go to **Spain**?

_____

_____

3. What is unique about Champlain's birth?

   A. He lived in a small village in France.
   B. The village he grew up in has changed names over the last 450 years.
   C. He was born when his parents were extremely old.
   D. Historians aren't quite sure when he was born.

4. According to the text, which country, army, or group did Champlain **never** serve?

   A. France
   B. Spain
   C. The Catholic Army
   D. The Huguenots

5. <u>How</u> did Champlain become commander of a boat in the **Spanish** navy, even though he was **French**?

_____

_____

_____

_____

Analyzing Point of View in Fiction (Pt.2)

Directions: On Day 1, you analyzed point of view in your **favorite** work of fiction. Today, you'll stretch your thinking by looking at a **new** fictional text. It could be a book, a short story, a movie, an episode of a television show, etc., but it should be something you've never read or seen before! Read or watch your fictional text, then answer the questions below to help you think about point of view!

1. Text Title: _____

- What happens in the text you selected? Write a short summary:

  _____

  _____

  _____

  _____

- Is the text written in **first-** or **third-person?** Who is the narrator, if they are identified?

  _____

  _____

- Are there any times in the story when the narrator shows **bias**, either in favor of or against any of the characters?

  _____

  _____

- What does this narrator's point of view provide **that you might not get if someone else was the narrator?**

  _____

  _____

- Pick <u>your favorite character</u> from the story who is **not** the narrator. How would the way the story is told be **different** if your favorite character was the narrator instead?

_____

_____

_____

_____

fitness

Please be aware of your environment and be safe at all times. If you cannot do an exercise, just try your best.

Repeat these **exercises** **4 ROUNDS**

2 - Side Bending: 15 times to each side. Note: try to touch your feet.

1 - Squats: 20 times. Note: imagine you are trying to sit on a chair.

3 - Tree Pose: Stay as long as possible. Note: do the same with the other leg.

MatH

Statistics

Use the graph below to answer questions 1-4.

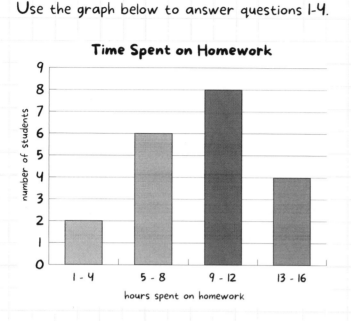

Time Spent on Homework

number of students / hours spent on homework

1. How many students spent less than 9 hours on homework?

   A. 4   C. 8
   B. 6   D. 12

2. How many students spent 9 hours or more on homework?

   A. 14   C. 10
   B. 12   D. 8

3. Which interval has the greatest frequency?

   A. 9-12   C. 1-4
   B. 13-16   D. 5-8

4. What was the total number of students surveyed?

   A. 16   C. 20
   B. 18   D. 22

Use the graph to answer questions 5-9.

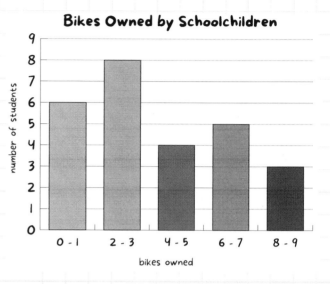

Bikes Owned by Schoolchildren

number of students / bikes owned

5. Which interval has the most frequency?

   A. 0-1   C. 4-5
   B. 2-3   D. 6-7

6. Which interval has the lowest frequency?

   A. 2-3   C. 6-7
   B. 4-5   D. 8-9

7. How many people own 4 or more bikes?

   A. 6   C. 9
   B. 8   D. 12

8. How many people own fewer than 8 bikes?

   A. 9   C. 23
   B. 15   D. 28

9. What was the total number of students surveyed?

   A. 26   C. 18
   B. 24   D. 30

MatH

Use this graph to answer questions 10-13.

Cell Phone Prices

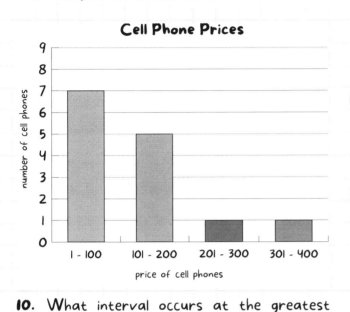

number of cell phones

price of cell phones

10. What interval occurs at the greatest frequency?

A. 201-300   C. 101-200
B. 1-100   D. 301-400

11. How many phones cost less than $200?

A. 12   C. 14
B. 13   D. 15

12. What percent of total phones cost $100 or less?

A. 95%   C. 25%
B. 75%   D. 50%

13. How many phones were examined?

A. 12   C. 14
B. 13   D. 15

14. Use the data below to make a frequency table of students' grades.

62, 83, 97, 93, 92, 69, 77, 72, 85, 87, 89, 94, 98, 66, 75, 82, 82, 74, 88, 80

Intervals	Frequency
62-70	
71-78	
79-87	
88-98	

15. Make a histogram for the data above.

---

fitness

Please be aware of your environment and be safe at all times. If you cannot do an exercise, just try your best.

Repeat these exercises **4 ROUNDS**

2 - Lunges: 12 times to each leg. Note: Use your body weight or books as weight to do leg lunges.

3 - Plank: 20 sec.

1 - Bend forward: 15 times. Note: try to touch your feet. Make sure to keep your back straight and if needed you can bend your knees.

4 - Abs: 20 times

MatH

Statistics

Use the box and whisker plot below to answer questions 1-5.

Hours Spent on Homework

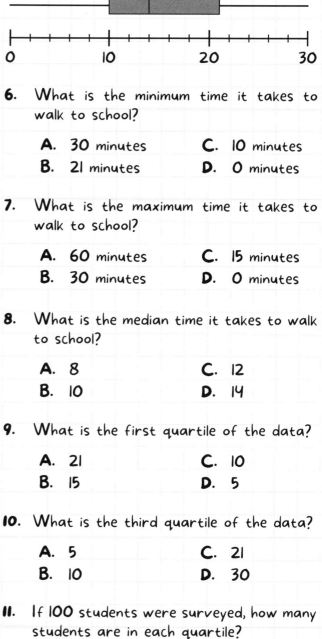

Raw Data: 5, 5, 5.5, 6.5, 7, 7, 7, 8, 10, 10, 15, 20

1. What is the interquartile range?

    A. 4   C. 6

    B. 5   D. 7

2. What is the median?

    A. 4   C. 6

    B. 5   D. 7

3. The majority of students spent how much time on homework?

    A. 5-6 hours   C. 7-10 hours

    B. 6-10 hours   D. 10-20 hours

4. How many students spent between 5 and 6 hours on homework?

    A. 3   C. 5

    B. 4   D. 6

5. Which amount of time did more than 5 students spend on homework?

    A. 6-7 hours   C. 10-20 hours

    B. 5-7 hours   D. 7-20 hours

Use the box and whisker plot below to answer questions 6-11.

Time it Takes to Walk to School (in minutes)

6. What is the minimum time it takes to walk to school?

    A. 30 minutes   C. 10 minutes

    B. 21 minutes   D. 0 minutes

7. What is the maximum time it takes to walk to school?

    A. 60 minutes   C. 15 minutes

    B. 30 minutes   D. 0 minutes

8. What is the median time it takes to walk to school?

    A. 8   C. 12

    B. 10   D. 14

9. What is the first quartile of the data?

    A. 21   C. 10

    B. 15   D. 5

10. What is the third quartile of the data?

    A. 5   C. 21

    B. 10   D. 30

11. If 100 students were surveyed, how many students are in each quartile?

    A. 25   C. 75

    B. 50   D. 100

12. Review the data set below. What is the median?

98, 84, 88, 76, 45, 56, 60, 65, 72, 77, 81, 92, 85, 78

A. 77   C. 78
B. 77.5   D. 98

13. What is the interquartile range of the grades?

A. 50   C. 30
B. 40   D. 20

14. The majority of scores fall between which range?

A. 85-98   C. 65-85
B. 77-85   D. 45-65

15. Use the data in question 12 to construct a box and whisker plot below.

fitness

Please be aware of your environment and be safe at all times. If you cannot do an exercise, just try your best.

Repeat these **exercises 4 ROUNDS**

1 - High Plank: 25 sec.

2 - Chair: 20 sec. Note: sit on an imaginary chair, keep your back straight.

3 - Waist Hooping: 20 times. Note: if you do not have a hoop, pretend you have an imaginary hoop and rotate your hips 10 times.

4 - Abs: 25 times

Statistics

1. Liam surveyed his classmates and found that 16 prefer pizza, 10 prefer hamburgers and 3 prefer tacos. Which measure of center best describes the data?

    A. Median   **C.** Mean

    B. Mode   **D.** Range

2. The data below represents the number of tickets a movie theater sold each day for one month. Which measure of center best describes the data?

266, 276, 289, 288, 289, 301, 302, 303, 321, 334

    A. Median   **C.** Mode

    B. Mean   **D.** Range

3. Which measure of variability is best for describing the data below?

64, 67, 67, 68, 68, 68, 69, 69, 69, 69, 70, 70, 70, 70, 70, 70, 71, 71, 71, 71

    A. Interquartile range

    B. Mean absolute deviation

    C. Mean

    D. Median

4. Which measure of variability is best for describing the data below?

9, 9, 10, 10, 10, 11, 11, 11, 11, 12, 12, 12, 12, 12, 12, 13, 13, 13, 13, 13, 13, 14, 14, 14, 14, 15, 15, 15, 16, 16

    A. Mean

    B. Median

    C. Mean absolute deviation

    D. Interquartile range

Use the line plot below to answer questions 5 and 6.

5. Which measure of center is best for describing the distribution of the data?

    A. Interquartile range

    B. Mean absolute deviation

    C. Median

    D. Mean

6. Which measure of variability is best for describing the distribution of data?

    A. Interquartile range

    B. Mean absolute deviation

    C. Median

    D. Mean

7. Which statement describes a data set for which the range would be the best measure of variability?

    A. A coach records the number of points made by players of each game of the season.

    B. A shop manager records the number of customers each day to find the least and greatest numbers.

    C. A teacher asks students to name their favorite color and records the number for each color.

    D. A bakery records the number of cakes sold each day over a 2-week period.

8. The list below shows the test scores for students in a class. Which statement is true?

88, 79, 45, 92, 89, 47, 93, 81, 88, 91, 83, 95, 78, 89, 93, 97, 87, 86

A. Its center is best described by its median.
B. Its center is best described by its mode.
C. Its variability is best described by its range.
D. Its variability is best described by its mean absolute deviation.

9. Which data set has a variability that is best described by its interquartile range?

A. 22, 24, 23, 24, 23, 25, 22, 25, 23, 23
B. 8, 10, 11, 7, 9, 12, 10, 9, 10, 10
C. 18, 18, 20, 19, 18, 19, 21, 42, 20, 18
D. 15, 17, 16, 14, 14, 16, 17, 15, 14

Use the box below to answer questions 10 and 11.

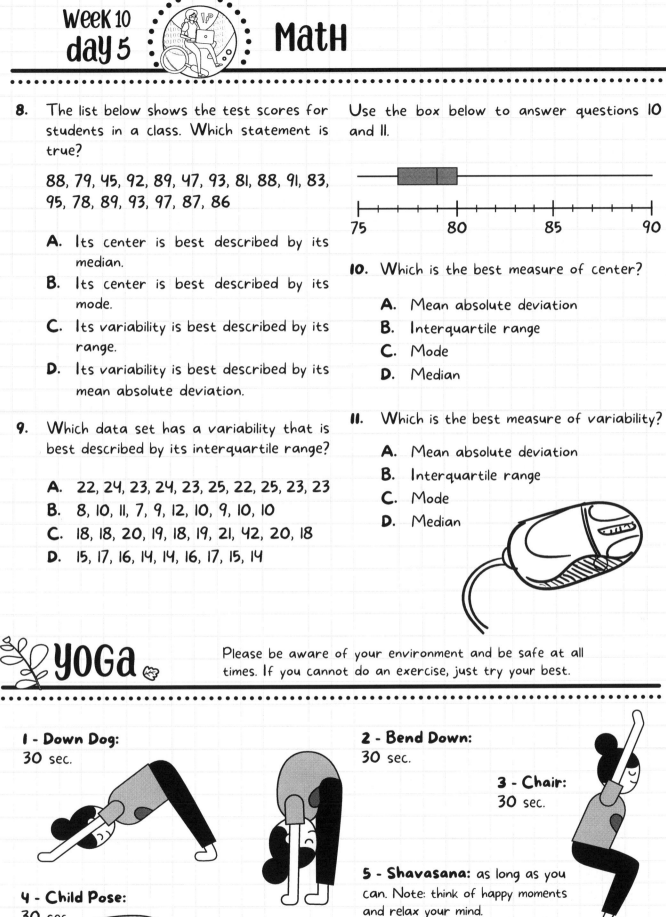

10. Which is the best measure of center?

A. Mean absolute deviation
B. Interquartile range
C. Mode
D. Median

11. Which is the best measure of variability?

A. Mean absolute deviation
B. Interquartile range
C. Mode
D. Median

yoga

Please be aware of your environment and be safe at all times. If you cannot do an exercise, just try your best.

1 - Down Dog: 30 sec.

2 - Bend Down: 30 sec.

3 - Chair: 30 sec.

4 - Child Pose: 30 sec.

5 - Shavasana: as long as you can. Note: think of happy moments and relax your mind.

Plant Cells

Throughout the summer, you've thought a lot about how **plants** and **animals** survive in their ecosystems. This week, however, we're going to start thinking on a **microscopic level** and think about the building blocks of the organisms in the world around us. All living organisms are made up of **cells.** Some tiny, microscopic organisms are literally only a single cell. On the other hand, the human body is made up of more than 37 trillion cells.

Over the past few centuries, scientists have identified that one of the biggest differences between **plants** and **animals** is that they have different kinds of cells. Over the next few weeks, you'll create two different models that will help you understand the difference.

Materials:

- Art supplies (markers, colored pencils, etc.)
- 1 shoebox
- Multicolored pipe cleaners
- Construction paper (multiple colors)
- Glue and/or masking tape
- A ping pong ball or small foam sphere
- Modeling Clay (optional but useful)
- Encyclopedias or internet access (for research)
- Plain white paper

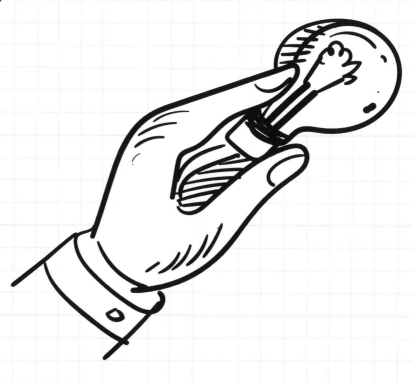

experiment

Procedure:

1. Begin by removing the lid from your shoebox and covering the outside and inside of the lower portion of the box using green construction paper and glue or tape. This represents the outer **cell wall** of the plant cell you'll be creating.

2. Using the internet for research, search for diagrams of plant cells. Study the names of the cell parts or "organelles" contained within a plant cell. You can even look at pictures of some different plant cell models people have created in the past.

3. After looking at some examples of plant cells, use your art materials and a little online research to create the following organelles and place them in the cell correctly: **Cytoplasm, Endoplasmic Reticulum, Mitochondria, Chloroplasts, Golgi Apparatus, Lysosome, and Ribosome**. You can draw them in, use modeling clay, bend pipe cleaners into the appropriate shape, or include any other appropriate materials that you have around the house. The **ping pong ball or foam sphere** in your materials represents the cell's **nucleus!**

4. After all your organelles are placed, create a small **key** or **legend** (like you would get on a map or graph) on your plain white paper to help people understand what they're looking at when they view your plant cell.

5. Answer the questions below, clean up your materials, and save your Plant Cell model to compare to an Animal Cell next week!

Follow-Up Questions:

1. Based on your research, explain the function of **at least three** different organelles in a plant cell:

_____

_____

_____

2. Based on what you read and saw as you created your model, how do you **predict** animal cells might be <u>different</u> from plant cells?

_____

_____

_____

yoga

Please be aware of your environment and be safe at all times. If you cannot do an exercise, just try your best.

3 - Stretching: Stay as long as possible.
Note: do on one leg then on another.

2 - Down Dog: 30 sec.

4 - Lower Plank: 20 sec.
Note: Keep your back straight and body tight.

6 - Shavasana: 5 min.
Note: this pose is very important and provides you with long term benefits. Try not to skip this. Close your eyes and imagine who you want to be and what your goals are! Always think happy thoughts.

1 - Tree Pose: Stay as long as possible. Note: do on one leg then on another.

5 - Book Pose: 20 sec.
Note: Keep your core tight. Legs should be across from your eyes.

Task: Take a look at the image below. If we fold this image, it will form a cube. Which of the following pictures is a possible representation of the cube in image 1?

Note: There is more than one correct answer.

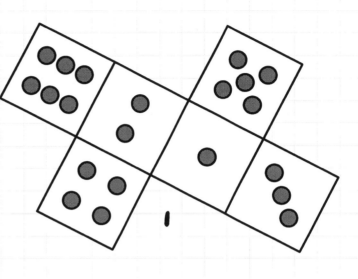

1

2

3

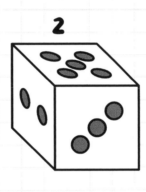

4

5

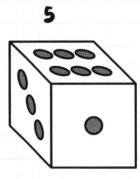

6

7

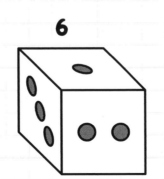
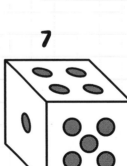

WEEK 11

Tracking Character Growth

When you read complex **fictional or literary texts**, understanding the <u>characters</u> is just as important as understanding the <u>plot</u>. Too often, readers focus on what happens in the story rather than thinking about who it happens to and how it affects those people. This week, we'll focus on **character growth**.

In most stories, the main character (also known as the **protagonist**) grows and changes through the course of their journey. Often, they begin the story as innocent, naive, inexperienced, or as an outsider; then, by the end of the story, they are experienced, capable, and self-assured. Other characters may begin the story in a position of power and be brought low by the end; still others may begin the story in a humble position but rise in power and importance. Regardless of what **changes** happen, it's your job as a reader to track them!

How Characters Grow
Before we start tracking the growth of any characters, let's take a look at what situations or forces within a text can cause a character to grow:
* **Mentorship from other characters** – A lot of the time, a young or inexperienced hero will meet some sort of **role model**, **coach**, **or wise figure** who teaches them how to navigate the world better.
* **Overcoming ordeals** – Typically, heroes and main characters are constantly facing **tests** -- either obstacles they must overcome, problems they must solve, or enemies they must defeat. Generally, passing those challenges involves **applying their skills or brainpower in new ways** and showing that they're capable of things they couldn't do previously.
* **Loss** – While it's sad to think about in real life, losing something or someone important often changes the way people look at the world. Many times in fiction, a character will experience a major change when they lose an important aspect of their life. Oftentimes, it will be **another character (like their mentor)**, or the loss could take the form of **not getting something they really wanted**.

Tracking Character Growth
Part of being a good reader is following the journey of how a character (especially the protagonist) grows and changes. Here are a few tools and strategies that can help you do it!
* Keep a **character diary** – This is really helpful for long texts. After each chapter or section of the text, write two or three sentences explaining how the characters are different than they were in previous chapter. Think about how their **attitudes**, **physical appearance**, and **way of looking at the world** evolve over the course of the story.
* Think about what the character is like **at the beginning** and then what they're like **at the end**. That will help you appreciate the major ways in which the character has grown or changed. After you've done that, try revisiting the middle sections of the texts to try and figure out which moment or situation caused that change.

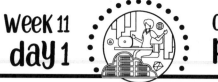

From "The Makers of Canada: Champlain"

By N.E. Dionne

(**NOTE:** This passage is from a later section of the same text you read during Week 10.)

After his return to France in the year 1601, Champlain received a pension, together with the appointment of geographer to the king. Pierre de Chauvin, Sieur de Tontuit, who had unsuccessfully endeavored to establish a settlement at Tadousac, died at this time, while Champlain was residing in Paris. Here he had the good fortune to meet Aymar de Chastes, governor of the town and château of Dieppe, under whose orders he had served during the latter years of the war with the League.

De Chastes, who had resolved to undertake the colonization of Canada, obtained a commission from the king, and formed a company, composed of several gentlemen and the principal merchants of Rouen. François Gravé, Sieur du Pont, who had already accompanied Chauvin to Canada, was chosen to return there and to examine the Sault St. Louis and the country beyond.

"Going from time to time to see the Sieur de Chastes," writes Champlain, "judging that I might serve him in his design, he did me the honor to communicate something of it to me, and asked me if it would be agreeable to me to make the voyage, to examine the country, and to see what those engaged in the undertaking should do. I told him that I was very much his servant, but that I could not give myself license to undertake the voyage without the commands of the king, to whom I was bound, as well by birth as by the pension with which His Majesty honored me to enable me to maintain myself near his person, but that, if it should please him to speak to the king about it, and give me his commands, that it should be very agreeable to me, which he promised and did, and received the king's orders for me to make the voyage and make a faithful report thereof; and for that purpose M. de Gesvres, secretary of his commandments, sent me with a letter to the said Du Pont-Gravé, desiring him to take me in his ship and enable me to see and examine what could be done in the country, giving me every possible assistance."

Champlain wrote, "I leave Paris and take passage on Pont-Gravé's ship in the year 1603, the 15th of the month of March." The voyage was favorable for the first fifteen days, but on the 30th a heavy storm arose, "more thunder than wind," which lasted until April 16th. On May 6th the vessel approached Newfoundland, and arrived at Tadousac on the 24th. Here they met with about one hundred natives, under the command of Anadabijou, who were rejoicing on account of their recent victory over the Iroquois. The chief made a long speech, speaking slowly. He congratulated himself upon his friendship with the French nation, and stated that he was happy to learn that the king was anxious to send some of his subjects to reside in the country and to assist them in their wars. Champlain was also informed that the Etchemins, the Algonquins, and the Montagnais, to the number of about one thousand, had lately been engaged in warfare with the Iroquois, whom they had vanquished with the loss of one hundred men.

1. What was **Aymar de Chastes'** role in Champlain's life?

_____

_____

_____

_____

2. How did Champlain **feel** about being sent to Canada?

_____

_____

_____

_____

3. Why could Champlain not say yes to Aymar de Chastes right away?

   A. He didn't have the money to go on the journey yet.
   B. He wasn't sure if colonizing Canada was a good idea.
   C. He needed permission from the king.
   D. He wasn't sure if he wanted to spend time away from his family.

4. Based on the passage, where is **Tadousac?**

   A. France
   B. Spain
   C. Puerto Rico
   D. Canada

5. How is the version of Champlain in **this passage** different from the way he was in Week 10 Day 1's passage?

_____

_____

_____

_____

Tracking Character Growth (Pt. 1)

Directions: Think of one of your **favorite** works of **fiction** (but try to choose a different one than you did when you talked about point of view!). It could be a book, a short story, a movie, an episode of a television show, etc. Take a few minutes to reflect on your experience with that text; then answer the questions below to help you think about how the main character in that story grew or changed. **NOTE:** It may be useful to have the text with you as you work, in case you need to check anything!

1. **Text Title:** _____

- What is the **protagonist** (main character) like at the <u>beginning</u> of the story? Describe their personality and habits on the lines below:

    _____

    _____

    _____

    _____

- Which **other character**(s) serve as **mentors** to your protagonist and help them <u>learn, grow, and figure out how to navigate the world</u> in new ways?

    _____

    _____

- Name **one** crucial moment in the text where a character solves a problem, defeats an enemy, or overcomes adversity using skills or knowledge they have learned in the course of their journey:

    _____

    _____

- What is the **protagonist** like at the <u>end</u> of the story? Describe their personality and habits at the <u>end</u> of the story on the lines below:

_____

_____

- Give an example of something the protagonist accomplishes **later** in the text that they wouldn't have been capable of **earlier** in the text:

_____

_____

_____

_____

 **fitness**   Please be aware of your environment and be safe at all times. If you cannot do an exercise, just try your best.

Repeat these exercises **4 ROUNDS**

2 - Lunges: 8 times to each leg. Note: Use your body weight or books as weight to do leg lunges.

1 - Abs: 20 times

4 - Run: 50m Note: Run 25 meters to one side and 25 meters back to the starting position.

3 - Plank: 20 sec.

From "The Makers of Canada: Champlain"

By N.E. Dionne

(Continued from Day 1's Passage)

Champlain now proceeded to explore the river Saguenay for a distance of twelve to fifteen leagues, and he thus describes the scenery: —

"All the land I have seen is composed of rocks, covered with fir woods, cypress, birch, very unpleasing land, where I could not find a league of plain land on each side." He also learned from the Natives of the existence of Lake St. John, and of a salt sea flowing towards the north. It was evidently Hudson Bay to which these northern tribes directed Champlain's attention, and if they had not seen it themselves they had probably heard of its existence from the Natives dwelling around the southern or south-western shores of the bay, who came annually to Nemiscau Lake to trade their furs. This lake was half way between Hudson Bay and the river St. Lawrence. The Kilistinons and other Natives of the north had regular communication with their colleagues scattered along the shores of the St. Maurice and the several rivers which flow into Lake St. John.

When the French arrived in Canada with Chauvin, in the year 1600, they began to monopolize the fur trade of all the Indian nations, but some years later the English established themselves on the shores of Hudson Bay, and carried out the trade for their own benefit.

Champlain could not, evidently, have been in possession of any exact information as to the existence of this large bay, as he was searching for a northern passage to China, the great desire of all the navigators and explorers of the time.

After having promised to aid the various tribes gathered at Tadousac in their wars, Champlain and Pont-Gravé proceeded to Sault St. Louis. This expedition lasted fifteen days, during which they saw Hare Island, so named by Jacques Cartier, and the Island of Orleans. The ship anchored at Quebec where Champlain stopped to make a short description of the country watered by the St. Lawrence, and they then proceeded to Sault St. Louis. Here Champlain gathered much valuable information relating to lakes Ontario and Erie, the Detroit River, Niagara Falls, and the rapids of the St. Lawrence. Returning to Tadousac, he determined to explore Gaspesia, and proceeded to visit Percé and Mal Bay, where he met Natives at every turn. He also was informed by Prévert, from St. Malo, who was exploring the country, of the existence of a copper mine.

Champlain carefully noted all the information he had received, and after his return to Tadousac he sailed again for France on August 16th, 1603, and reached Havre de Grâce, after a passage of twenty-one days.

1. How did **Champlain** describe the geography and natural features of Canada?

_____

_____

_____

2. <u>How</u> did Champlain **gather information** about where the different lakes, rivers, and bays of Canada were located?

_____

_____

_____

3. According to the passage, who benefitted most from the Hudson Bay fur trade?
   A. The English
   B. The French
   C. The Spanish
   D. The Natives

4. According to the text, what was Champlain trying to find in Canada?
   A. Furs
   B. Gold
   C. Copper
   D. A route to China

5. Based on the passage, what **important information** did Champlain bring back to France?

_____

_____

_____

_____

_____

Tracking Character Growth (Pt. 2)

Directions: On Day 1, you analyzed character growth in your **favorite** work of fiction. Today, you'll stretch your thinking by looking at a **new** fictional text. It could be a book, a short story, a movie, an episode of a television show, etc., but it should be something you've never read or seen before! Read or watch your fictional text, then answer the questions below to help you think about character growth!

1.   Text Title: _____

- What is the **protagonist** (main character) like at the beginning of the story? Describe their personality and habits on the lines below:

  _____

  _____

  _____

  _____

- Which **other character**(s) serve as **mentors** to your protagonist and help them <u>learn, grow, and figure out how to navigate the world</u> in new ways?

  _____

  _____

- Name **one** crucial moment in the text where a character solves a problem, defeats an enemy, or overcomes adversity using skills or knowledge they have learned in the course of their journey:

  _____

  _____

- What is the **protagonist** like at the <u>end</u> of the story? Describe their personality and habits at the <u>end</u> of the story on the lines below:

_____

_____

- Give an example of something the protagonist accomplishes **later** in the text that they wouldn't have been capable of **earlier** in the text:

_____

_____

_____

_____

fitness

Please be aware of your environment and be safe at all times. If you cannot do an exercise, just try your best.

Repeat these **exercises 4 ROUNDS**

2 - Side Bending: 15 times to each side. Note: try to touch your feet.

1 - Squats: 20 times. Note: imagine you are trying to sit on a chair.

3 - Tree Pose: Stay as long as possible. Note: do the same with the other leg.

Ratios and Proportions

1. Justin drive 132 miles in 4 hours. What is the unit rate?

   A. 54 mph
   B. 48 mph
   C. 43 mph
   D. 33 mph

2. Graham has a marble collection with 31 blue marbles and 24 red marbles. What is the ratio of red marbles to the total number of marbles in his collection?

   A. $\dfrac{24}{31}$

   B. $\dfrac{31}{55}$

   C. $\dfrac{24}{55}$

   D. $\dfrac{31}{24}$

3. A basketball player made 5 free throws and missed 3 free throws. What is the ratio of the number of missed free throws to the total number of free throws shot?

   A. 5 : 5
   B. 5 : 8
   C. 3 : 8
   D. 3 : 5

4. Marcus bought 7 hats for $172.13. If each hat cost the same amount, what was the price of one hat?

   A. $29.59
   B. $29.02
   C. $24.59
   D. $25.01

5. The sales tax on a television is 5% of its price. The television costs $1000. What is the amount of the sales tax?

   A. $50
   B. $5
   C. $1050
   D. $1500

6. A florist has 40 tulips and 32 roses. What is the ratio of tulips to total flowers?

   A. 72 to 40
   B. 40 to 72
   C. 32 to 72
   D. 32 to 40

7. Amanda rides 45 miles in 3 hours. If she continues to ride at the same pace, how far will she ride in 5 hours?

   A. 30 miles
   B. 60 miles
   C. 15 miles
   D. 75 miles

8. Which ratio is equivalent to 3:21?

   A. 6 : 24
   B. 1 : 18
   C. 1 : 7
   D. 6 : 40

9. Which fraction is equivalent to 40%?

   A. $\dfrac{2}{5}$

   B. $\dfrac{1}{4}$

   C. $\dfrac{4}{5}$

   D. $\dfrac{1}{20}$

MatH

10. What is 18% of 150?

A. 27   C. 28
B. 38   D. 18

11. There are 20 students in May's homeroom. Ten percent of the students in May's homeroom are also in her art class. How many students are in her art class and her homeroom?

A. 1   C. 3
B. 2   D. 4

12. A bakery makes 200 bagels each day. 45% of the bagels are plain. How many bagels are plain?

A. 75   C. 85
B. 80   D. 90

13. Brian drove 180 miles to his grandparents' house. He drove 30% of the trip before lunch. How many miles did he drive after lunch?

A. 60 miles   C. 126 miles
B. 30 miles   D. 54 miles

14. There are 40 vehicles in the school parking lot. 40% are trucks. How many vehicles are trucks in the parking lot?

A. 16   C. 20
B. 18   D. 22

15. Which statement is true?

A. 12 is 5% of 60.
B. 6 is 12% of 200.
C. 30 is 3% of 100.
D. 15 is 30% of 50.

Please be aware of your environment and be safe at all times. If you cannot do an exercise, just try your best.

Repeat these exercises **4 ROUNDS**

2 - Lunges: 12 times to each leg.
Note: Use your body weight or books as weight to do leg lunges.

3 - Plank: 20 sec.

1 - Bend forward: 15 times.
Note: try to touch your feet. Make sure to keep your back straight and if needed you can bend your knees.

4 - Abs: 20 times

Number Systems

1. What is $\frac{11}{12} \div \frac{3}{4}$

   A. $\frac{11}{16}$

   B. $1\frac{2}{9}$

   C. $\frac{2}{9}$

   D. $1\frac{11}{16}$

2. Divide $3.02 \div 6.04$

   A. 0.25
   B. 0.5
   C. 0.67
   D. 0.42

3. Which number is closest to 0 on a number line?

   A. 3
   B. -9
   C. -2
   D. 4

4. What is the opposite of 3?

   A. -3
   B. $\frac{1}{3}$
   C. 1
   D. 0

5. Multiply $1.9 \times 3.4 \times 0.05$

   A. 32.2
   B. 3.23
   C. 0.232
   D. 0.323

6. Subtract $150,201 - 9,487$

   A. 182,820
   B. 159,352
   C. 141,821
   D. 140,714

7. Which choice equals $32 + 48$

   A. $3 \times (4 + 12)$
   B. $7 \times (2 + 24)$
   C. $8 \times (4 + 6)$
   D. $12 \times (3 + 7)$

8. Add: $405.2 + 18.09$

   A. 423.29
   B. 58.61
   C. 21.49
   D. 424.1

9. Which of the following could be represented by a negative number?

   A. A store marks up the price of a calculator.
   B. A football team's first play resulted in a loss in yards.
   C. Nina deposited her allowance into her bank account.
   D. A bird is flying high above sea level.

10. Which comparison is a false statement?

   A. $-6 > -8$
   B. $|-6| < |-8|$
   C. $|-6| < -8$
   D. $-6 < |-8|$

11. Aaron has 24 squash plants and 18 corn plants that he is going to plant. Each row will contain one type of plant and he wants to have the same number of plants in each row of the garden. He wants the greatest number of plants possible in each row. How many plants will each row contain?

A. 8   C. 6

B. 3   D. 12

12. Mrs. Gatz is making bird feeders. Each feeder needs a piece of wood that is $9\frac{1}{2}$ inches long. She has two pieces of wood. One is 4 feet long and one is $18\frac{3}{4}$ inches long. What is the greatest number of birdhouses she can make out of a single piece of wood?

A. 5   C. 7

B. 6   D. 8

13. What is the least common multiple of 6 and 21?

A. 42   C. 3

B. 6   D. 126

14. What is the greatest common factor of 32 and 48?

A. 8   C. 4

B. 16   D. 6

15. There are 351 students going on a middle school field trip. The students will ride on buses that hold 64 students each. How many buses will the school need?

A. 3   C. 5

B. 4   D. 6

fitness

Please be aware of your environment and be safe at all times. If you cannot do an exercise, just try your best.

Repeat these exercises **4 ROUNDS**

1 - High Plank: 25 sec.

2 - Chair: 20 sec. Note: sit on an imaginary chair, keep your back straight.

3 - Waist Hooping: 20 times. Note: if you do not have a hoop, pretend you have an imaginary hoop and rotate your hips 10 times.

4 - Abs: 25 times

Expressions and Equations

1. Which value is equal to the difference of 12 and the product of 3 squared and 3?

    A. -12
    B. 15
    C. 12
    D. -15

2. What is the value of $(5 + 7) \div 2 + 4^2$?

    A. 18
    B. 20
    C. 22
    D. 24

3. Which expression represents 5 more than the product of 4 and 1 less than a number?

    A. $4(n - 1) + 5$
    B. $4n - 1 + 5$
    C. $4n - 2$
    D. $4n + 5$

4. Which word describes the meaning of the number 14 in the expression $14m + 6 - n$?

    A. Variable
    B. Term
    C. Product
    D. Coefficient

5. Which expression does not represent the algebraic expression $2(n + 5)$?

    A. Twice the sum of n and 5
    B. Two times the sum of n and 5
    C. The quotient of 2 and 5 more than n
    D. The product of 2 and 5 more than n

6. Carlos gave the cashier $20 to buy 3 posters costing p dollars each. Which algebraic expression shows the amount of change he would receive?

    A. $20 - 3p$
    B. $3p - 20$
    C. $20 + 3p$
    D. $20p - 3$

7. Evaluate $6x - 3(x + 2y)$ for $x = 4.3$ and $y = 0.1$.

    A. 12.3
    B. 11.3
    C. 10.3
    D. 9.3

8. Solve $(2x^3 + 4) \div (2x + 2)$ for $x = 3$.

    A. 6.25
    B. 6.75
    C. 7.25
    D. 2.5

9. Which expression is equivalent to $2(a - 7)$?

    A. $16a$
    B. $a - 14$
    C. $2a - 7$
    D. $2a - 14$

10. The length of a rectangle is 4 more than its width. Which expression represents the area of a rectangle?

    A. $2w + 4$
    B. $w(w + 4)$
    C. $4w$
    D. $4w + 4$

MatH

11. What value of x makes 5x - 4 equivalent to 2(x + 4)?

A. 4
B. 3
C. 2
D. 1

12. Solve for x: 15x = 45

A. x = 3
B. x = 2
C. x = 5
D. x = 2

13. Solve for y: y - 6 = 22

A. y = 22
B. y = 26
C. y = 28
D. y = 30

14. Solve for a: 14 - a < 5

A. a < -9
B. a > -9
C. a < 9
D. a > 9

15. In which equation is y not the dependent variable?

A. y = 4x
B. 1.5 + x = y
C. x - 12 = y
D. 9y = x

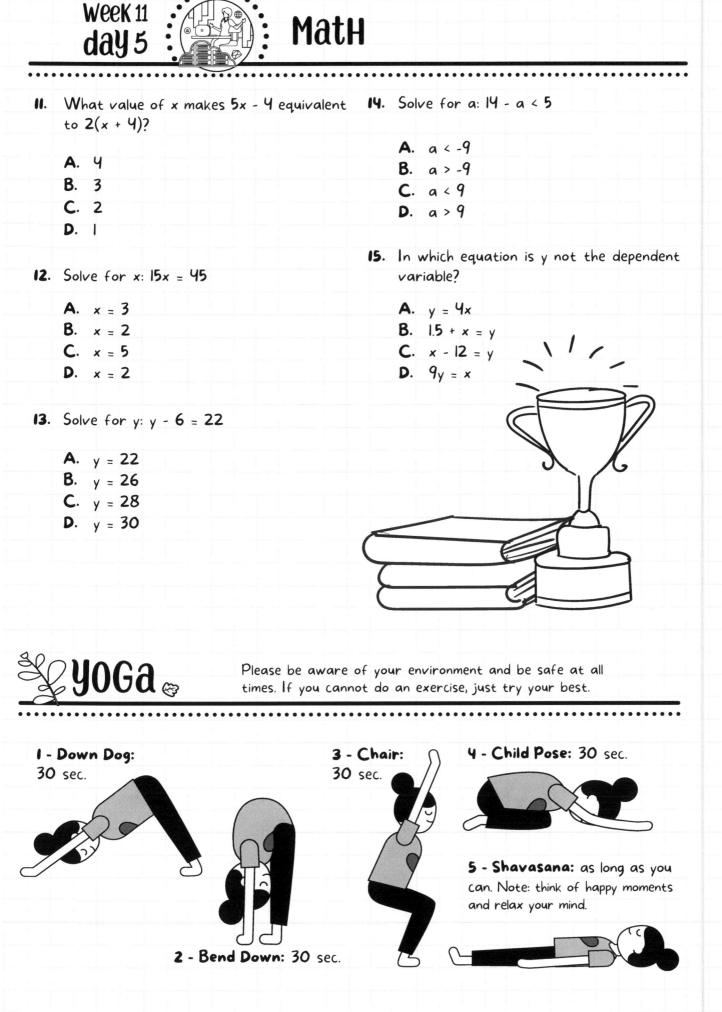

yoga

Please be aware of your environment and be safe at all times. If you cannot do an exercise, just try your best.

1 - Down Dog: 30 sec.

2 - Bend Down: 30 sec.

3 - Chair: 30 sec.

4 - Child Pose: 30 sec.

5 - Shavasana: as long as you can. Note: think of happy moments and relax your mind.

235

Animal Cells

Last week, you created a model of a **plant cell** using independent research and some crafting skills. This week, you'll continue to increase your knowledge of cells by creating an **animal cell**. Like we said last week, the tiniest animals can be made of just one cell. However, the animals we encounter in our daily lives contain billions or trillions.

Animal cells have a completely different structure from plant cells. They **do not** have the same rigid outer cell wall that plant cells do (think of the edges of your shoebox), and although they contain many of the same **organelles**, there are also several key differences. As you complete this activity, focus on the differences between creating this animal cell and the process you went through to create your plant cell last week.

Materials:

- 1 large foam sphere (available at a craft store – 12" to 18" in size is ideal)
- Several smaller foam balls of assorted sizes
- Art supplies (Markers, colored pencils, etc.)
- Tempera paint (with brushes and water)
- Multicolored pipe cleaners
- Modeling Clay (optional but useful)
- A craft knife (and an adult to use it)
- A piece of plain white paper
- Your Plant Cell model (created in Week 11's activity)

Procedure:

1. Start by **having an adult** use the craft knife to cut into the large foam sphere at a 45-to-90 degree and remove the resulting wedge of foam, creating an "open mouth" that looks like a certain classic video game character. (If you or your adult is having trouble visualizing this, simply search "Animal Cell Model" on the internet, and you'll see a variety of different ways to cut your foam ball.)

2. Once your sphere has a slice in it, use the tempera paint to paint the outside edges of the foam sphere. This represents your animal cell's **Cell Membrane.**

3. Using the internet for research, search for diagrams of animal cells. Study the names of the cell parts or "organelles" contained within an animal cell. You can even look at pictures of some different animal cell models people have created in the past.

4. After looking at some examples of animal cells, use your art materials and a little online research to create the following organelles and correctly place them in the "mouth" of the animal cell you've just created: **Nucleus, Cytoplasm, Endoplasmic Reticulum, Mitochondria, Golgi Apparatus, Vacuole, Lysosome, and Ribosome.** You can use foam or modeling clay to create these organelles, bend pipe cleaners into the appropriate shape, or include any other appropriate materials that you have around the house.

5. After all your organelles are placed, create a small **key** or **legend** (like you would get on a map or graph) on your plain white paper to help people understand what they're looking at when they view your animal cell.

6. Clean up your art supplies and work area.

7. Compare your Animal Cell and Plant Cell models side-by-side and answer the questions below.

experiment

Follow-Up Questions:

1. Name at least **two key similarities** between this model and the plant cell model you created last week:

_____

_____

_____

2. Name at least **two specific differences** between this model and the plant cell model you created last week:

_____

_____

_____

 ## yoga

Please be aware of your environment and be safe at all times. If you cannot do an exercise, just try your best.

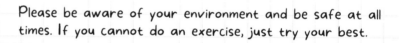

3 - Stretching: Stay as long as possible. Note: do on one leg then on another.

2 - Down Dog: 30 sec.

4 - Lower Plank: 20 sec. Note: Keep your back straight and body tight.

1 - Tree Pose: Stay as long as possible. Note: do on one leg then on another.

6 - Shavasana: 5 min. Note: this pose is very important and provides you with long term benefits. Try not to skip this. Close your eyes and imagine who you want to be and what your goals are! Always think happy thoughts.

5 - Book Pose: 20 sec. Note: Keep your core tight. Legs should be across from your eyes.

Task: Take a look at the picture below and write your own story on a separate piece of paper. Use your imagination to write an amazing story.

Approaching Poetry

We've discussed and reviewed a variety of literary and informational texts over the last 11 weeks, but we haven't spoken at all about a different kind of writing: **poetry!** Poetry is a genre that uses **lines** and **stanzas** rather than traditional sentences and paragraphs, which means it looks significantly different on the page from **prose**, a term used to discuss any writing that **isn't** poetry.

Poetry is a lot less straightforward than prose, in that the goal of prose is generally to make ideas as clear as possible for the reader. Poetry, on the other hand, intentionally seeks to make the reader grapple with their thoughts, feelings, and emotions to construct meaning of their own. Since there's so much "work" involved in comprehending poetry, it's incredibly important to **read closely!** Today, we'll introduce some strategies you can use to make poetry more accessible.

Key Terms
Prose: Any form of writing that is not poetry (a short story, a biography, etc.)
Poetry: A literary genre based on thoughts, feelings, emotion, and rhythm
Line: A single line of text in a poem (but not necessarily a full sentence!)
Stanza: A grouping of connected **lines** that serves like a <u>paragraph</u> in poetry

Poetry-Reading Strategies:
- When you read poetry, **don't** read it one line at a time; read it **one sentence at a time**
  - Look for **end punctuation** (. ! ?) to find the end of the first "sentence" in the poem
  - Then, trace back to the beginning of the sentence, read it through, and begin your analysis that way
  - Continue to move through the poem one sentence at a time in this way
- Make **lots** of notes as you read and reflect
  - Using notes helps you remember what you took away from each line or sentence, so when you're done with the poem, you can review all of your notes to get a full sense of things
- When you reach the end of a **stanza**, pause to <u>think about the stanza as a whole</u>
  - Just like you do when you read a **paragraph** in prose!
- Read and think about the text **multiple times**
  - As we've said before, poetry can be a little more complex than prose, but poems are also generally **shorter**, so it's easy to read them <u>several</u> times in a single session. Those repeat readings reinforce comprehension and give you multiple attempts to consider the author's meaning or intentions.

One More Tip!
- One of the biggest secrets to poetry is **not being intimidated by it!**
  - At first, it might just seem like a random collection of pretty-sounding lines, but once you've built an understanding of just a few of those lines, things will begin to fall into place and the poem will become much more accessible. You just need to believe in yourself and keep reading!

"The Light of Stars"

By Henry Wadsworth Longfellow

(**NOTE:** In addition to being a planet in our solar system, "Mars" was also the name of the Roman god of war.)

The night is come, but not too soon;
And sinking silently,
All silently, the little moon
Drops down behind the sky. (4)

There is no light in earth or heaven
But the cold light of stars;
And the first watch of night is given
To the red planet Mars. (8)

Is it the tender star of love?
The star of love and dreams?
O no! from that blue tent above,
A hero's armor gleams. (12)

And earnest thoughts within me rise,
When I behold afar,
Suspended in the evening skies,
The shield of that red star. (16)

O star of strength! I see thee stand
And smile upon my pain;
Thou beckonest with thy mailed hand,
And I am strong again. (20)

Within my breast there is no light
But the cold light of stars;
I give the first watch of the night
To the red planet Mars. (24)

The star of the unconquered will,
He rises in my breast,
Serene, and resolute, and still,
And calm, and self-possessed. (28)

And thou, too, whosoe'er thou art,
That readest this brief psalm,
As one by one thy hopes depart,
Be resolute and calm. (32)

O fear not in a world like this,
And thou shalt know erelong
Know how sublime a thing it is
To suffer and be strong. (36)

1. What activity is the **narrator** or **speaker** of the poem describing?

_____

_____

_____

_____

2. How does the **note** provided at the top of the text <u>change or clarify</u> your understanding of the poem?

_____

_____

_____

_____

3. Which object in the night sky is the narrator most focused on?

   A. The moon
   B. The big dipper
   C. Mars
   D. Clouds

4. What is the **"brief psalm"** described in **Line 30?**

   A. The night sky
   B. The planet Mars
   C. The poem itself
   D. The narrator's sense of hope

5. What **life lesson** does the narrator take away from his experience looking at the planet Mars?

_____

_____

_____

_____

Practicing Poetry Comprehension

Directions: Read the poem below **one stanza at a time** and use the strategies from the concept overview to ensure you comprehend what's going on in each section. After you read each stanza, **craft a short "summary" or explanation of that stanza** in the box to its right. Once you've read and summarized/explained all 7 stanzas, read your summaries together, then create an overall summary/explanation in the box at the bottom of the page.

Woods in Winter
By Henry Wadsworth Longfellow

When winter winds are piercing chill,
  And through the hawthorn blows the gale,
With solemn feet I tread the hill,
  That overbrows the lonely vale.

Stanza 1:

O'er the bare upland, and away
  Through the long reach of desert woods,
The embracing sunbeams chastely play,
  And gladden these deep solitudes.

Stanza 2:

Where, twisted round the barren oak,
  The summer vine in beauty clung,
And summer winds the stillness broke,
  The crystal icicle is hung.

Stanza 3:

Where, from their frozen urns, mute springs
  Pour out the river's gradual tide,
Shrilly the skater's iron rings,
  And voices fill the woodland side.

Stanza 4:

Alas! how changed from the fair scene,
  When birds sang out their mellow lay,
And winds were soft, and woods were green,
  And the song ceased not with the day!

Stanza 5:

But still wild music is abroad,
   Pale, desert woods! within your crowd;
And gathering winds, in hoarse accord,
   Amid the vocal reeds pipe loud.

Chill airs and wintry winds! my ear
   Has grown familiar with your song;
I hear it in the opening year,
   I listen, and it cheers me long.

Stanza 6:

Stanza 7:

Overall Summary:

fitness

Please be aware of your environment and be safe at all times. If you cannot do an exercise, just try your best.

Repeat these **exercises 4 ROUNDS**

1 - Abs: 20 times

2 - Lunges: 8 times to each leg.
Note: Use your body weight or books as weight to do leg lunges.

3 - Plank: 20 sec.

4 - Run: 50m
Note: Run 25 meters to one side and 25 meters back to the starting position.

"The End"

By D.H. Lawrence

IF I could have put you in my heart,
If but I could have wrapped you in myself,
How glad I should have been!
And now the chart
Of memory unrolls again to me.   (5)
The course of our journey here, before we had to part.

And oh, that you had never, never been
Some of your selves, my love, that some
Of your several faces I had never seen!
And still they come before me, and they go,   (10)
And I cry aloud in the moments that intervene.

And oh, my love, as I rock for you to-night,
And have not any longer any hope
To heal the suffering, or make requite
For all your life of asking and despair,   (15)
I own that some of me is dead to-night.

1.   Based on the <u>first stanza</u>, what is the narrator **thinking about or reflecting on** in this poem?

_____

_____

_____

_____

2. Why do you think the poet chose to end Stanza 1 with the word "part"?

    _____

    _____

3. Which of these things does the poet seem to **regret** in Stanza 2?

    A. That he was ever in love
    B. That he saw the worst sides of someone he loved
    C. That he never really got to know the person he loved
    D. That the person he loved was a two-headed monster

4. Which of these best describes the overall mood of the poem?

    A. Uplifting
    B. Mysterious
    C. Romantic
    D. Melancholy

5. In the poem's final line, why do you think the narrator states, "something of me is **dead** tonight?

    _____

    _____

    _____

    _____

Crafting a Poem

Directions: Now that you've had a chance to read and engage with some poetry, it's time to **write a poem of your own!** First, think of what **topic** or **theme** you will explore. Then, start writing! Be sure to break your poem into **at least two stanzas** and write **sentences that carry on for more than just one line**. Feel free to use the poems you've read this week as inspiration, or you can research some more poetic styles on your own before you get started.

TITLE: _____

_____

_____

_____

_____

_____

_____

_____

_____

_____

_____

_____

_____

_____

_____

_____

_____

fitness

Please be aware of your environment and be safe at all times. If you cannot do an exercise, just try your best.

Repeat these **exercises 4 ROUNDS**

1 - Squats: 20 times. Note: imagine you are trying to sit on a chair.

2 - Side Bending: 15 times to each side. Note: try to touch your feet.

3 - Tree Pose: Stay as long as possible. Note: do the same with the other leg.

Geometry

1. A trapezoid has vertices located at (-2, 4), (4,4), (7, -2) and (-5, -2). What is the area of the trapezoid?

   A. 52   C. 56
   B. 54   D. 64

2. Four parallelograms are below. Which parallelogram does not have an area of 88 square units?

   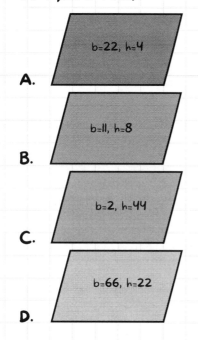

   A. b=22, h=4

   B. b=11, h=8

   C. b=2, h=44

   D. b=66, h=22

3. Which set of dimensions describes the rectangular prism with the smallest surface area?

   A. Length = 15, Width = 15, Height = 15
   B. Length = 9, Width = 17, Height = 2
   C. Length = 12, Width = 6, Height = 4
   D. Length = 10, Width = 10, Height = 3

4. A triangle is located at (2, 3), (2, 7) and (11, 3). How much longer is the base of the triangle in the graph than the height?

   A. 9   C. 4
   B. 8   D. 5

Use the diagram below to answer questions 5-7.

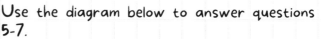

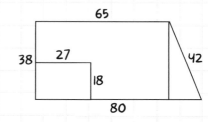

5. The plan above is of a garden. What is the total area of the garden?

   A. 2,755   C. 475
   B. 2,470   D. 2,095

6. The small rectangle will be a fountain. How much grass will be needed to cover the garden?

   A. 2,954   C. 2,269
   B. 2,549   D. 2,945

7. If the farmer wants to put a fence around the garden, what is the perimeter of the garden?

   A. 231   C. 229
   B. 236   D. 225

8. A rectangular prism has a volume of 36 cubic inches. Its base has an area of 24 square inches. What is its height?

   A. 1.5 inches   C. 3.5 inches
   B. 5.3 inches   D. 5.1 inches

9. Which of the following three-dimensional figures could have a net which consists of two squares and four rectangles?

   A. Triangular pyramid
   B. Rectangular pyramid
   C. Rectangular prism
   D. Triangular prism

10. Which shape has the same area as the triangle below?

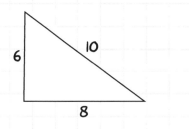

A. Parallelogram with base of 6 and height of 5

B. Square with sides of 5

C. Rectangle with base of 8 and height of 3

D. Trapezoid with bases of 6 and 8 and height of 4

11. Denise makes a set of trapezoidal earrings. The height of the earrings is 3 cm. The bases are 1 cm and 3 cm. What is the total area of both earrings?

A. 3

B. 6

C. 12

D. 24

12. A rectangular prism has a volume of 4,704 centimeters cubed. Its height is 21 cm. What is the area of the prism's base?

A. 224

B. 228

C. 234

D. 238

13. Franny has a storage box with a length of 70 centimeters, a depth of 36 centimeters and a height of 29 centimeters. What is the volume of this storage box?

A. 62,404

B. 68,202

C. 71,080

D. 73,080

14. Point J is plotted at (1, -3), point F is plotted at (-3, 2) and point G is plotted at (5, 2). What is the area of FGJ?

A. 10   B. 20   C. 30   D. 40

15. Which shape has the greatest number of faces?

A. Triangular prism

B. Rectangular prism

C. Square pyramid

D. Triangular pyramid

fitness

Please be aware of your environment and be safe at all times. If you cannot do an exercise, just try your best.

Repeat these exercises **4 ROUNDS**

2 - Lunges: 12 times to each leg. Note: Use your body weight or books as weight to do leg lunges.

3 - Plank: 20 sec.

1 - Bend forward: 15 times. Note: try to touch your feet. Make sure to keep your back straight and if needed you can bend your knees.

4 - Abs: 20 times

Statistics

Use the line plot below to answer questions 1-4.

Sports Play by Students in our Class

1. What is the outlier of the data?

   A. 6
   B. 5
   C. 4
   D. 3

2. What is the range of the data?

   A. 7
   B. 6
   C. 5
   D. 4

3. What is the median of the data?

   A. 1
   B. 2
   C. 3
   D. 4

4. How many students were surveyed?

   A. 24
   B. 25
   C. 27
   D. 29

Use the whisker plot box below to answer questions 5-8.

Weight of Babies Born in June

5. What was the heaviest weight of babies born?

   A. 11 lbs
   B. 12 lbs
   C. 13 lbs
   D. 14 lbs

6. What was the median weight of babies born?

   A. 6 lbs
   B. 7 lbs
   C. 8 lbs
   D. 9 lbs

7. The majority of babies born in June were how large?

   A. 7-8 lbs
   B. 9-12 lbs
   C. 8-12 lbs
   D. 12-13 lbs

8. What is the best measure of center?

   A. Median
   B. Mean
   C. Range
   D. Mode

Use the histogram below to answer questions 9-12.

Points Scored

9. How many students played the game in all?

   A. 15
   B. 16
   C. 17
   D. 18

10. The majority of students scored how many points?

    A. Less than 20
    B. More than 60
    C. Less than 40
    D. More than 40

11. What was the smallest amount of points students scored?

    A. 3   C. 0-19
    B. 60-79   D. 1

12. Which score would not be represented by this histogram?

    A. 82   C. 39
    B. 46   D. 60

Use the line plot below to answer questions 13-15.

Gym attendance

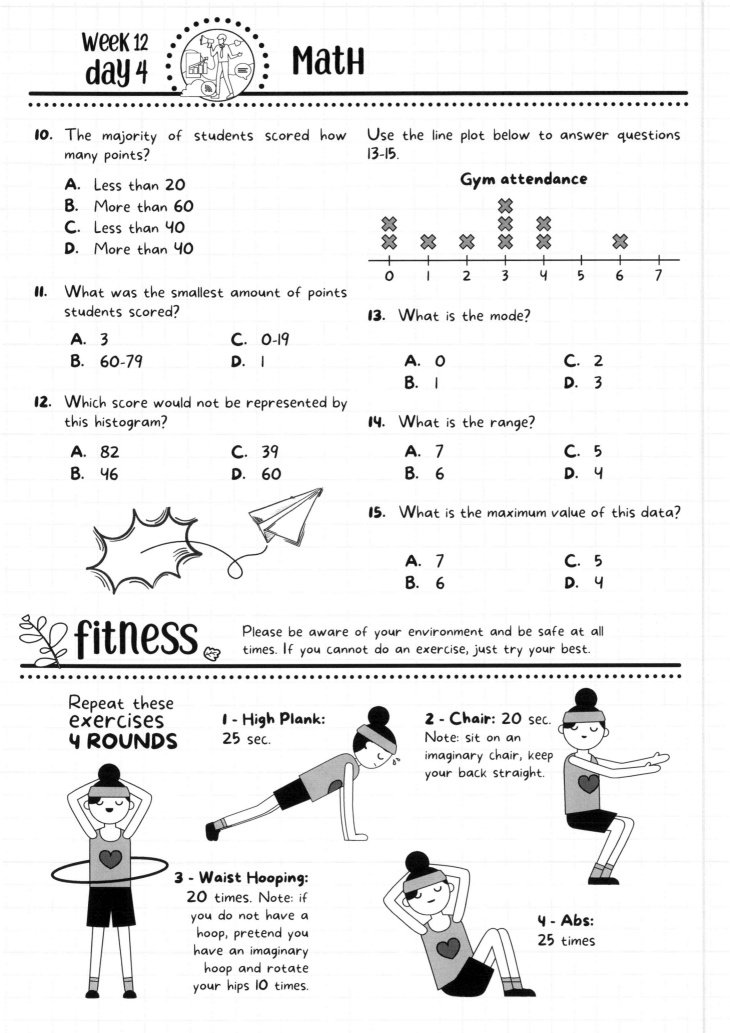

13. What is the mode?

    A. 0   C. 2
    B. 1   D. 3

14. What is the range?

    A. 7   C. 5
    B. 6   D. 4

15. What is the maximum value of this data?

    A. 7   C. 5
    B. 6   D. 4

---

fitness

Please be aware of your environment and be safe at all times. If you cannot do an exercise, just try your best.

Repeat these **exercises 4 ROUNDS**

1 - High Plank: 25 sec.

2 - Chair: 20 sec.
Note: sit on an imaginary chair, keep your back straight.

3 - Waist Hooping: 20 times. Note: if you do not have a hoop, pretend you have an imaginary hoop and rotate your hips 10 times.

4 - Abs: 25 times

MatH

Mixed Review

Use the following information to solve problems 1-3.

There are 28 students in Mr. Bianca's homeroom. 16 of those students are girls.

1. What is the ratio of girls to boys?

A. 16 : 12   C. 16 : 28

B. 12 : 16   D. 12 : 28

2. Which ratio is not equivalent to the ratio of boys to total students?

A. 12 to 28   C. 3 to 7

B. 6 to 14   D. 16 to 12

3. Mr. Bianca's students represent 16% of the whole school. How many students are in the whole school?

A. 160   C. 170

B. 165   D. 175

Use the following chart to answer questions 4-6.

Day	Temperature (°F)
Monday	8
Tuesday	-2
Wednesday	-9
Thursday	0
Friday	1

4. Which day had the coldest temperature?

A. Thursday   C. Wednesday

B. Monday   D. Friday

5. Which day had the warmest temperature?

A. Thursday   C. Wednesday

B. Monday   D. Friday

6. How many days was the temperature below freezing?

A. 5   C. 2

B. 3   D. 0

7. What is the value of twelve squared divided by the difference of eleven and two?

A. 16   C. 12

B. 14   D. 8

8. The expression $p - 0.4p$ can be used to find the price of an item on sale for 40% off the original price. What is the sale price of a dress with an original price of $75.95?

A. $5.99   C. $37.48

B. $29.98   D. $45.57

9. Solve for n: $\frac{n}{3} = 12$

A. n = 9   C. n = 36

B. n = 6   D. n = 24

10. A rectangular prism has a volume of 4,896 cubic cm. Its base has an area of 306 square centimeters. What is its height?

A. 14 cm   C. 18 cm

B. 16 cm   D. 22 cm

11. A polygon has vertices at (-5, 3), (-2, 2), (-2, -2) and (-5, -3). What shape is formed?

A. Trapezoid   C. Rectangle

B. Triangle   D. Pentagon

12. The area of one face of a cube is 49 square centimeters. What is the surface area of the cube?

A. 49 cm²

C. 343 cm²

B. 2401 cm²

D. 294 cm²

Use the box and whisker plot below to answer questions 13-15.

Number of states students visited

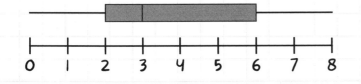

13. What is the median number of states visited by students?

A. 1

C. 3

B. 2

D. 4

14. What is the minimum number of states visited by students?

A. 1

C. 8

B. 0

D. 4

15. What is the interquartile range of the data?

A. 7

C. 3

B. 4

D. 2

 Yoga

Please be aware of your environment and be safe at all times. If you cannot do an exercise, just try your best.

1 - Down Dog: 30 sec.

2 - Bend Down: 30 sec.

3 - Chair: 30 sec.

4 - Child Pose: 30 sec.

5 - Shavasana: as long as you can. Note: think of happy moments and relax your mind.

Nerve Cells & Neurons

Over the last couple of weeks, you've expanded your understanding of **cells** and their role in the world of living **plants** and **animals**. Within **complex** organisms (like people, animals, and large plants), cells begin to specialize and take on specific tasks. For example, within your body, a group of specialized cells makes up your liver. Those cells are specifically created to handle the responsibilities of the liver. Similarly, your skin is made up of specialized cells that are designed to form an effective barrier around your body. In short, although all things are made of cells, they may actually be made up of numerous, very different types of cells!

Today you'll be creating a model of a **neuron**, which is a specialized cell within the **nervous system. Neurons** are responsible for communicating information back and forth between our brains and the rest of our bodies at lightning speed. When you grab something sharp, **neurons** help communicate that message of pain to your brain, which in turn tells your hand "Let go of that sharp thing!"

Materials:

- Modeling clay (a few different colors is best)
- An encyclopedia or internet access (for research)
- A ping pong ball or small foam sphere
- String
- Scissors
- A few pipe cleaners
- A few plastic beads
- Plain white paper
- Art supplies (colored pencils, markers, etc.)

Procedure:

1. Begin by taking your ping pong ball and wrapping it in modeling clay, creating a slightly larger sphere. This represents the cell body or **soma** of the neuron, which contains the nucleus and all the other <u>organelles</u> you learned about in Week 11's Animal Cell activity. Since this is a specialized neuron and not just a generic cell, there's lots more work to do, though!

2. Cut a length of string, insert one end in the clay around your soma, and cover the length of the string in clay. This represents the **axon** or tail of your neuron.

3. Using the internet for research, search for diagrams and pictures of neurons. Study the names of the different parts of the neuron and look at their characteristic shape.

4. After looking at some examples of neurons, use your art materials and some online research to create and attach the additional parts of the neuron: **Dendrites**, **Myelin Sheath** (beads may be helpful here), and **axon terminals.**

5. After all your neuron parts are placed, create a small **key or legend** (like you would get on a map or graph) on your plain white paper to help people understand what they're looking at when they view your neuron

6. Clean up your art supplies and work area.

7. Compare your neuron to your Animal Cell model from Week 11 and answer the questions below.

experiment

Follow-Up Questions:

1. How is the **neuron model** you created different from your **animal cell** model?

_____

_____

_____

2. If neurons conduct **electricity**, how is the **myelin sheath** like the rubber insulation frequently used on electrical wires?

_____

_____

_____

yoga

Please be aware of your environment and be safe at all times. If you cannot do an exercise, just try your best.

3 - Stretching: Stay as long as possible. Note: do on one leg then on another.

4 - Lower Plank: 20 sec. Note: Keep your back straight and body tight.

2 - Down Dog: 30 sec.

6 - Shavasana: 5 min. Note: this pose is very important and provides you with long term benefits. Try not to skip this. Close your eyes and imagine who you want to be and what your goals are! Always think happy thoughts.

5 - Book Pose: 20 sec. Note: Keep your core tight. Legs should be across from your eyes.

1 - Tree Pose: Stay as long as possible. Note: do on one leg then on another.

GOALS

Task: Write down 10 goals you would like to accomplish this year.

GOAL #1

GOAL #2

GOAL #3

GOAL #4

GOAL #5

GOAL #6

GOAL #7

GOAL #8

GOAL #9

GOAL #10

Answer Sheets

To see the answer key to the entire workbook, you can easily download the answer key from our website!

*Due to the high request from parents and teachers, we have removed the answer key from the workbook so you do not need to rip out the answer key while students work on the workbook.

All you need to do is:

Step 1 - Visit our website at: **www.argoprep.com/books**

Step 2 - Choose the workbook you have and you will see **DOWNLOAD ANSWER SHEETS** button as well as all video explanations.

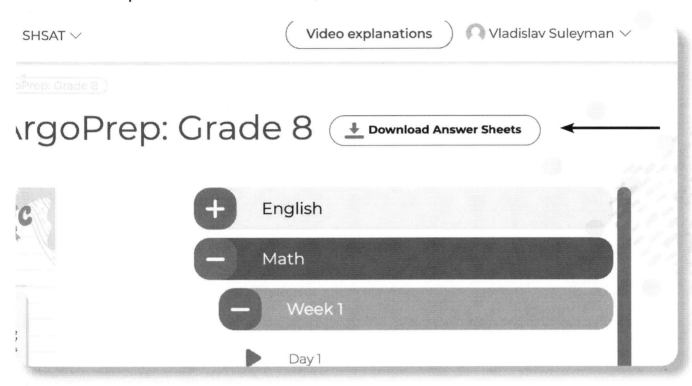

Made in the USA
Monee, IL
10 June 2021